# — THE —
# TREE
## IN CHANGING
## LIGHT

Also by Roger McDonald

FICTION

*1915*
*Slipstream*
*Rough Wallaby*
*Water Man*
*The Slap*
*Mr Darwin's Shooter*

NON-FICTION:

*Shearer's Motel*

AS EDITOR:

*Gone Bush*

# THE
# TREE
## IN CHANGING
## LIGHT

*Roger McDonald*

Wood engravings by Rosalind Atkins

**v**
VINTAGE

The writing of this work was assisted by a fellowship from the Australia Council, the Federal Government's arts funding and advisory board.

A Vintage Book
Published by Random House Australia Pty Ltd
20 Alfred Street, Milsons Point, NSW 2061
http://www.randomhouse.com.au

Sydney   New York   Toronto
London   Auckland   Johannesburg

First published in Australia by Knopf, an imprint of Random House Australia, 2001.
This Vintage edition first published 2002.

National Library of Australia
Cataloguing-in-Publication Entry

McDonald, Roger, 1941-.
The tree in changing light.

ISBN 1 74051 181 6 (pbk).

Trees – History. 2. Forests and forestry – History. 3.
Trees – Social aspects. 4. Plants and civilization. I.
Atkins, Rosalind. II. Title.

333.75

Wood engravings © Rosalind Atkins.
Cover design by Peter Long.
Internal design by Greendot Design.
Typeset in 12 pt Adobe Garamond by Midland Typesetters, Maryborough, Victoria
Printed and bound by Griffin Press, Netley, South Australia

10 9 8 7 6 5 4 3 2 1

'No genuine book has a first page. Like the rustling of a forest, it is begotten God knows where, and it grows and it rolls, arousing the dense wilds of the forest until suddenly, in the very darkest, most stunned and panicked moment, it rolls to its end and begins to speak with all the treetops at once.'

# Contents

# PLANTING OUT

'Whatever happened, there would remain the feeling
underneath, the shape of a tree where no tree was
before. It regathered itself and insisted on thickening
into life. The planter appeared, arms out like branches,
trunk measured against trunk, head moving
against the stars . . .'

IT HAPPENED best after good soaking rain in well-drained soil holding moisture to a useful depth. Behind the chugging tractor the ripper blade in a shining 'J' dragged along on the lumpy dirt. Movement started, the ripper lowered and bit, the metal shaft went into the ground barely breaking a seal. Slicing through parting clumps of grass it unfurled a polished banner of continuous earth. Bundles of grass roots were sectioned; worms divided. Forward of the point where the cut peeled open a swelling ran as if a subterranean animal were under there smoothly plummeting through the paddock and hurrying ahead to keep out of the way.

Planters followed with bundles of seedlings in plastic tubes and dropped them at intervals against the furrow. It happened quickly, what happened next—the transition from which comes momentous change (or may); a spade levering earth at an angle; the planter dropping to the knee, or to both knees in a quick unconscious plea for life backed by a dirty-fingernailed routine of plastic casing off, naked root-shaft palmed this way or that, then into the ground, a bit rough;

planting out was like that. Over. And on to the next one all morning, all afternoon, until a stitching of feathery-topped seedlings counted in hundreds, and then in thousands, embroidered the paddock and ran over the hill and into the dark.

What might come of this could only be guessed. Some time later a forest? Birdlife and the layering of ecology once cleared out? Or simple failure and starting over again—no further rain this season; massed insect attack; wandering stock trampling and feeding—the dry stars overhead like so many wasted seeds.

Whatever happened, there would remain the feeling underneath, the shape of a tree where no tree was before. It re-gathered itself and insisted on thickening into life. The planter appeared, arms out like branches, trunk measured against trunk, head moving against the stars.

Germination was a spark of light. Seed, fine as ground pepper, scattered and struck. Seedlings emerged through leaf matter glistening with dew.

Shoots slithered from the ground as delicately as fine hair. Two small leaves parted and bared themselves to light. The evolving architecture of the tree began. Angle of branch, buckled fold of bark, shaggy river of red sap. It was the seedling giving consideration to the elements, designing itself into the sky with tree after tree undulating along the ridge.

'The tree grew not by stretching elastically (like a leech) but step by step, by means of addition or superimposition.

Although the living shoot of any year lengthened until it reached its terminal bud, after that bud was formed its length was fixed. It was thenceforth one joint of the tree, like the joint of a pillar, on which other joints of marble were laid to elongate the pillar, but which would not itself stretch. A tree was thus truly edified, or built, like a house.'

Leaves were solar collectors. They generated sugars that flowed through the inner bark and changed into the woody material of the branches, trunk, and roots. The slide of stored light (each year recorded in growth rings) was how the tree increased in size—with an effect like a candle coating itself and growing fatter at the base.

From the bare gate a kilometre off a particular tree on the high sandy plateau resembled a child's transfer. Scattered across the slope were others of the same species. Some showed brittle, skeletonised limbs and gappy, insect-eaten foliage. Others seemed to have been drawn with a snapped pencil. The light showed through all of them. As I drove closer the one tree thickened and spread, showing itself immense in the winter light. The way it played back and forth with scale, now puny, now enormous, was a conversation we had every time I drove the last kilometre. When I left the car the trunk rose sleek as marble, cold and weighted to the touch. Checking it over by feel, smoothing the bark, impressed by its elephant-like presence, I stepped back seeing what sticks had fallen while I was away (upper wood with a habit of loosing itself and crashing). There was a matting of twigs underfoot, a rain of firewood fallen among corkscrewed scrolls of bark and layered leaves. Out came a cardboard box and in moments enough kindling was gathered for the fire.

Inside the house the Warmray stove crackled with flame struck from the tree's stored light.

At night outside, trees led the eye back to the stars. The scatter of stars and the pattern of branches joined. The farthest bud and the farthest beginnings of life connected.

On summer nights tree insects swarmed. I went outside batting scarab beetles from my face and wondering where the roar of wind came from.

Moths on a windowpane held the shape of the tree behind them. The tree was a cut-out shadow against the stars. And the stars were a spiral of moths.

Clouds settled in the tops of trees. The fretworked tips of leaves and moisture droplets combined. So it rained under the trees, but nowhere else, condensation forming a drip line. Boys climbed the trees with the aim of getting higher. In their hearts they raced the clouds, though a poem could have told them:

> Too much rain
> loosens trees.
> In the hills giant oaks
> fall upon their knees.

You can touch parts
you have no right to—
places only birds
should fly to.

# WHERE THE FIRE
## HAS BEEN

'Right to the end we said we would
never leave . . .'

AT THE back of childhood, long before I was born, my mother ran alongside a paling fence with wet potato sacks, beating out flames that rushed through the grass towards her parents' farmhouse. Her mother was ill inside the house and her father was away fighting the fire on another front, where it was expected to be worse. Overhead the sky was a dense, scrolled blue, with ash and cinders raining down. Across the eucalypts at the far end of the paddocks orange sheets of flame shot up and exploded into leaf-heads of volatile oil in a crown fire. It had leapt the Glenelg river and only my mother was there to save the house.

Later when she rode her pony to school there were smouldering logs over the track, dead lizards in the ashes. I see her crossing a scorched plateau on a sturdy pony called Creamy, apprehensive yet curious, and not wanting to miss anything that was going on. She discounted any talk of bravery, doing what had to be done. All the while the river glimmered away below, bared to the sky by the peeling away of its fringing vegetation in the intensity of flame. There was a cool spring under the limestone cliffs where asparagus grew, clear water where roots went down and seedlings thrived among ferns.

The farm was on sandy soil, at Drik Drik, in Victoria. When my mother, Lorna, was eleven her father, my grandfather, Chester Bucknall, began dealing with the Forestry Pulp and Paper Co. Ltd., and started planting pines. He established a nursery, building a hydraulic ram and developing a watering system; it was slow but functioned day and night without any running cost. He supervised gangs of men planting out trees. My mother's eldest brother, Graeme, started work in the company as a forester. My grandfather was made a director and travelled to Geelong every quarter for board meetings. Over the next decade, the Depression years, he evolved from farmer to forester. After the war the farm was kept going by Fred, the next brother, but finally it was sold and now there are vast stands of pine over the whole district, and the farm itself, since around 1970, has disappeared under them.

Nobody, it seems, has a good word to say about *Pinus radiata*, but Chester Bucknall's were surely the best around, growing in sandy soil with good sub-surface water, producing straight, unblemished poles. Somebody made money from the trees, those firebreaked, numbered sections. It wasn't Chester Bucknall, who smoked a pipe and suffered from asthma, wore a soft felt hat and a suitcoat and tie when out and about, and had a mild, warm, ironic smile if I am to judge from his photographs. There is one where he holds me on his knee, a be-frocked infant of around twelve months of age. We lived in central-western New South Wales then, and he came up from Victoria to visit. He died when I was four, at the end of the Second World War. My mother inherited stock in the company and after forty years started getting a few small dividends. My grandfather was revered for who he was, a friendly man whose ambitions for his children were moral, spiritual, intellectual; a good mate to his daughter, who (after my grandmother's early death) was his companion on expeditions in a T-model Ford through the Grampian Ranges and along the Murray River, down to Adelaide and McLaren Vale.

When I meet older relations they say I am like Chester Bucknall. They mean the genetic inheritance of looks, mannerisms, tone of voice perhaps. Such doubles can mean anything. But might they also mean cast of mind? In which case, although I never really knew him, I believe him to have been a dreamer about trees. Other than a forester alone, that is.

My uncle, Graeme Bucknall, worked as a forester in Victoria and Tasmania before he became a theological student and a Presbyterian minister in the 1930s. As a young preacher he drove around Gippsland in the early years of World War II, burying the dead and cheering up the living with his genial calls. One day he heard about three specialist axemen hewing beams from grey box trees with broadaxes at Wroxham. The timber was being cut for a wartime extension to the Port Kembla jetty. Graeme drove his car down into the valley where the men were working. At smoko they got yarning about timber cutting and he asked them if they had ever used a 'bastard' file in a particular way to take the shoulder off an axe. They had not ever used one in this way; and so it was the ex-forester parson who demonstrated how to drive the back of the axe head into a narrow scarf and with the handle of the file bedded in the tree trunk, drag the file face over the shoulder of the axe until it cut into the steel with the filings coming away in minute strips.

Family history as it expresses itself in an individual can feel like something coming from nowhere, because the roots are buried. It is only now, in midlife, that I feel this matter of trees as part of a line of continuation. My mind sinks back; I go into the shade; it feels like drawing water up through fine capillary veins and having leaves uncurl, and then those leaves hanging edge-on to the hard Australian sunlight. I like to think of the earth around the roots being kept damp by a sprinkler disgorging cold, silver water.

Somewhere in my early childhood I absorbed images of an ideal bush. Two places come to mind. One was not bush-proper at all, but a backyard at the edge of an inland New South Wales town with a tennis court, some pepper trees, a few eucalypts dense enough to hide and play in, and (most importantly) to climb. I don't remember what variety they were, but they were aged enough to have hollows formed by fallen branches containing wild beehives, and other hollows big enough for a child to climb into. Water was on tap but always in short supply. On the outer edges of the trees, through a fence and across a dirt road, were wheatfields. They were well cleared except for a few ringbarked dead trees and dark, shimmering clumps of native cypress. In the harvest season around Christmas there were sheaves and haystacks to play in. Alternating images of enclosure, darkness, and hiding places, compared with openness, brightness, and distant views, were the contrasting combinations.

Though this first ideal image of bush was not native bush at all, but a Europeanised mongrel remnant, it is mostly what we meant in Australia when we used the term 'the bush' (which also meant everywhere outside the cities). It was on the outskirts of Temora, in central-western New South Wales.

The other image is more timeless in feel. It was a kangaroo-grass hillside at the back of a small Riverina town, with granite boulders among scattered wattles and gums, and with small shrubs hardening their seeds past their spring flowering. There was the incessant hum, hop, click and scratch of insects, and the constant presence of birds. It was not farmland but unwanted land, and so had survived as bush in the second sense. I do not know if it is still there. It was the season for sawfly grubs, who linked themselves in a long, rhythmic chain and jerked along the earth with the unity of a single organism, and other species endemic to eucalypts, including the ones called hairy caterpillars. We raced around dropping them inside each other's shirts, creating allergic reactions. From a slighly elevated position it was possible to look out over the town and west into the wider inland. Like a lot of bush it only existed to the passing eye in a good season, when it responded and burst into life. Otherwise it needed closer ways of looking to be understood. It was at Ardlethan, in the eastern Riverina.

I grew up a minister's son in central and western New South Wales. We lived at Bribbaree when I was born, then at nearby Temora, and finally at Bourke at the end of the western line. A move to Sydney came at the end of my primary school years, when my father left his parish ministry and became secretary to the New South Wales Board of Missions in the Church Offices, Assembly Hall, Margaret Street.

Here are images of trees gathered from a country childhood, recovered from the scrapbook of memory. Ironbarks along the fringe of a dry creekbed, blond summer grass in the foreground. The sap-stained trunks dark as if blood has been poured down them and aged into the fibrous material. The line of trees looking small in daytime, thrust down by light. But later, in the gunpowder-blue twilight, looming up as if they are walking closer. All this seen from the verandah of the manse at Bribbaree, a wooden house like a land-yacht in my perception of the way it rode unseparated from the country around.

There must have been a fence at Bribbaree but I don't remember any. Was I too small to see what I saw, being just a baby lying on a rug on the verandah boards? It is the picture I have—as with so many other fragments that are like guiding images in all of our lives, with missing parts demanding to be filled in by imagination. I saw the moon rise through the branches of trees, heard crickets, frogs, watched shadows shorten. I saw it first then—moonrise through trees—the sight that promised journeys in stillness, in storm, through broken cloud.

I remember trees away out in the smashed-glass glare of wheatfields: yellow box, white cypress, kurrajong. Lone sentinels shimmering in heat haze. And playground eucalypts in asphalt, their leaves pungent after rain. A tree at Bourke, it must have been a red gum, growing tall in the dirt-surfaced playground there; Aboriginal kids eating grubs from under the bark and boasting about it; our teacher taking us out to sit around under its thin shade and asking me to read out a story I had written—a 'composition'. I remember how everyone listened.

I remember visiting a homestead on the Darling River and staring at the orange trees: glossy leaves, creamy flowers, fruit with a skin thicker than coconut rind, flesh richer than any mango. Then up to the border at Hungerford, camping out under the stars, and my father naming the trees: leopard tree, bloodwood, wilga, quandong—peeling the sour red quandong flesh, insubstantial as a thumb-scraping, and drying the seeds that were ridged like a model of the human brain. We made a game of spotting leopard trees—their delicate distinctiveness was a prize in itself. Travelling through red sandhills my father waved his hat against the door of the car to attract emus. They came in their curious hundreds. Up there, north-west of Bourke, it was the beginning of the outback, except that 'outback' then was always somewhere farther on.

I revisited Bourke many years later. More accurately, I passed through in a rush on my way to Yantabulla, near Hungerford, on my way to my first appointment as a shearers' cook, which I tried as a break from writing in 1989 and described in *Shearers' Motel*. It was still possible to find the idealised landscape of my childhood out from the shearers' quarters in breaks between cooking. But the woody weeds from years of dry seasons and overgrazing were taking their toll. In places they showed as impenetrable stiff walls of low vegetation instead of the open parklike vistas of memory. There are beautiful descriptions of a landscape untouched by sheep in C.E.W. Bean's *On the Wool Track*, published early in the last century; but also contrasting depictions of the ravages to the thin topsoil by (at that time) at least fifty years of sheep grazing. Another ninety have passed since then and western New South Wales is often a depressing mishmash of claypans, scoured earth, woody weeds and burr patches. Other parts of the country—especially the towns, in terms of shade trees planted—look better than I remember them. Memory is deceptive, and many if not all good impressions in Australia depend on the season. To my eye, I was amazed by the number of trees across Bourke township. They added an oasis feel to what was always an outpost feel.

My father, Hugh Fraser McDonald, was a Queenslander, born and raised in Rockhampton. We visited Rocky from Bourke in the 1949 Chev for Christmas holidays that involved cross-country expeditions through back country. My brothers and I rode our uncles' old bikes around Rockhampton's hot, wide, empty streets. The insides of kitchens always smelled of ripening tropical fruit. Every backyard had mango trees and the fruit lay rotting on the ground. The ice-cream factory tried mango ice-cream but it had no appeal for locals. There were no other trees in Rocky, just acres of tin roofs and the mangoes, and bare yards where a battle was fought against encroaching tropical grasses, tough as tin. Rockhampton awaited the invention of the Victa lawn-mower, only then would it be suburbanised, losing its look of spare colonial calm.

After our move to Sydney the two senses of 'the bush'—first as the place where country people lived, and second as native forest (or scrub, more commonly)—receded to images of places with a strong nostalgic pull. After the first novelty the city had negative connotations. It was a long trudge to school and home again. Other elements were missing, difficult to define. I suppose the closest to a dreamscape was the Blue Mountains, where the Presbyterian church owned a large holiday house, 'Balqhain', in Govett's Leap Road, Blackheath. Off the main roads the bush then was like it is now: a gallery of charred banksias, scrolls and shards of eucalpyt bark, and secretive, tough little shrubs, starred with wildflowers, in shadowed crevices or hanging onto cliffs. Where the fire has gone reveals the essence of trees, as in all life.

My father's last parish was Hunters Hill, in Sydney. I was still at school. He was diagnosed with early-onset Parkinson's disease. It was a devastating time for my parents.

My father was forty-eight years old. His world closed in. He asked me if I had ever thought of being a minister. He would have been proud. Did he imagine I would continue some line of his, that he had never spoken to me about, or was unable to articulate? It was where his roots went down, not mine.

Within a decade his physical orbit was reduced to a few immediate concerns. He died in 1981. Too late the right questions came. Now I want to know what his self-image was. What was his tree?

I was seventeen, in my last year at Scots College, when I made a declaration: I wanted to be a forester. This took my parents by surprise. My father, his thinking shaped by a self-reliant childhood and the Depression years—and a new insecurity—wondered if I shouldn't leave school and work in a bank. As I recall, my mother argued against it. I was to go to university, it was not to be doubted. But *forestry*? I was a dreamer, the impractical son whose older brother did all his bicycle repairs for him, and whose chemistry set, a jumble of jars and powders, lay in a stained heap on a laundry shelf. I was the verbaliser of everything who had never shown any interest in gardening or horticulture, and indeed I cannot ever remember planting anything at all. Not even a pumpkin seed. All I can remember is watching other people do things and imagining how it must feel.

There was nothing in our life in Sydney that inspired this suddenly declared ambition, except, I suppose, the negative sense of suburban life in its man-made smallness compared with the pull of the outdoors. The astonishing bush of the Sydney sandstone region wasn't part of my immediate environment, except in pockets that seemed immeasurably small.

The requirements for forestry school were all science based. My parents sent me to the Institute of Industrial Psychology in Hunter Street, where I took a vocational guidance test. The counsellor told me that being a forester had nothing to do with a love of dank earth, long shadows, banks of trees on a river bend; nor of deep, dark recesses of stillness and peace where I could take my adolescent longings and sink into oblivion. My aptitudes, so comprehensively listed in a column and illustrated in bar graphs, were verbal: they belonged to a career in advertising, law, teaching, broadcasting, or scriptwriting. Until that day I had never thought of trees as timber, something to be made use of, beautiful in their growth but only coincidentally so. A forester was a technologist, it seemed.

I became the first person on my father's side of the family to go to university, became a teacher, worked in broadcasting. I worked as a book editor. Nothing felt settled until

I started writing novels and found myself living back in the country again.

It was night, a low full moon coming up through ribbon gums on a rocky ridge. I stood at the back door of the house and the moon was close, a huge dimmed torchlight. I was forty years old and had planted my first tree, a linden or European lime, on the three hundred and twenty acres of Spring Farm, Braidwood.

I went walking down the sweep of paddocks. Moonlight slipped through the hollows like milk. Lone trees stood silvery in semi-mist. Then other trees appeared. They were coming towards me—poplars, ribbon gums, peppermints and black-woods on their rocky rises—shapes with their illusion of strolling in the dark, almost affably, conversationally, mysteriously arriving. Spirits loosened. It happened in moonrise. Durran Durra Creek ran black along a sandy bottom. The moon rose higher, brighter, harder. This was during the El Niño event of the early 1980s, the worst drought on record. Where did the moisture come from, that made dry summer nights smell as if there had just been a sprinkle of rain? Granite boulders extruded from the decomposed granite soil. They were like huge eggs and exfoliated onion-heads. Eucalypts grew among them, snow gums and ribbon gums, peppermints and a few wattles. They were raggedy and insect-chewed. Neighbouring paddocks were bare. Sand-drifts covered the Euradux Road from town. The bare rocky moon was a desert moon.

We had hired a digger to scoop a hole in the trickling creek and lowered a concrete well-liner to hold water. I started bucketing water to trees. The sandy soil soaked it up. I had come around full circle. Now I could have what I wanted at seventeen—a dream of trees—and be living in that feeling at the same time. I didn't have to be scientific about it. I could try things out with trees, and if they didn't work I could try them in a different way.

Introduced trees had been planted at Spring Farm for well over a hundred years. As native trees were cleared the exotics went in. There were many Lombardy poplars, along with willows, black locusts or robinia, elms, hawthorns, Monterey cypresses, arbutus or Irish strawberry, Canary Island pine, and tree of heaven in a pungent, impenetrable stand. A neighbour in his eighties remembered the Lombardy poplars as big old trees when he was ten. They lined sections of creek and formed an avenue between the house and the shearing shed. Not once did they falter in the drought. They had their roots far down past layers of sand and into damp clay. Stretching a hundred feet high they made a sound of fluttery whispers when currents of air filtered past. It was a sound to fall asleep to. So was the sound of possums glissading on the corrugated iron roof of the shearing shed. In strong winds the same poplars thundered like surf. In the dark of still, clear nights, their leaf-spires sliced out sections of sky: canoe shapes, blades, candles. They were silent sentinels taking thoughts up to the stars. In spring they smelled of sweet honey. Equinoctial gales came with immense power and shook the poplars by the roots, and hauled back branches of eucalypts like a hand pulling bunches of hair. The house was positioned in a slight hollow and the worst winds curved over it. The ground rocked, slammed by the assault. I see the house sunk in its hollow, far back from any road, a dim light bulb burning outside the back door, black branches crashing in the dark. From down near the creek I hear the insistent flapping of tin at the pump shed.

The hardest frosts were then, at the start of the eighties. Minus fourteen degrees and the pipes all burst in the walls of the house, and a small side creek running into Durran Durra Creek was still frozen at four in the afternoon. I skidded stones on the ice and our first farm dog, Sheba, chased them. Her legs went everywhere on the muddy ice. At Jinglemoney, where we lived before Spring Farm, Sheba used to stand in the shade of a linden tree and stare into the dark for ten minutes at a time. The power of that linden with its heart-shaped leaves and silvery-green trunk, so beautifully growing on a sand-ridge in the garden above the river, inspired me to plant the one at Spring Farm. The one that failed.

The nitrogen-rich granite soil stretching ten or so kilo-metres out from Braidwood's Mount Gillamatong attracted land clearing early in white settlement. Alexander Harris in *Convicts and Settlers* records all the useful land being taken up by the 1820s. Spring Farm lies at the edge of a zone of almost total denudation. On rocky outcrops we had ribbon gums, a few peppermints, a few wattles, including blackwoods, and even a few stubborn banksias and heath species of shrub sur-viving where sheep and cattle had long grazed.

There were snow gums and black sallees with a habit of flecking their leaves silver in the bracing winter winds. But re-introducing native trees into that bleak, frost-exposed landscape was difficult. There was no longer the over-storey and under-storey of compatible, protective varieties to give even an open-forest concept a new start. I concentrated on propagating *Eucalyptus viminalis* seeds from a magnificent old ribbon gum near the house, and had most success with those, planting them in rows near the creek. The hardiest eucalypt I planted wasn't local—the Camden woolly butt or *Eucalyptus macarthurii*. They were more resistant to Christmas beetle attack which converted many young viminalis into what looked like toilet brushes, and invariably slowed their growth. To get the most reliable responses, and also in sympathy with the already Europeanised look to the landscape, I concentrated in those first years on introduced varieties.

Even so, at the back of my mind, there was a constant speculation about what this sandy but fertile plateau would have been like in pre-European times. It would have been environmentally rich country, holding its moisture in a delicate topsoil despite the sharp drainage of the soil type. I had a fantasy, never fulfilled, of getting some of the paddocks back to the way the landscape would have once looked. A reedy creek, wildfowl, banksias despite the fierce cold, and glittering black sallees in the frost hollows—a tree with an almost mystical attachment to the coldest places, with olive and green tones in the bark, almost like streamed shellacked paint. Here and there in the paddocks, at a rate of a few to the acre, there would have been huge old ribbon gums—or water gums to use an old common name for them. I saw them swarming with native beehives.

Among tree planters various ways have been devised to get native trees back onto farms. They all involve hard work, disappointment, an investment of money and, most of all, take individual determination. Even then there is often failure.

With Landcare—where ideas once thrust on farmers are worked through by them—some of the hopeless isolation landholders feel about trees is met with neighbourly collaboration: costs, materials and labour no longer feel like odds stacked against good intentions. (Landcare is an Australia-wide, community-based approach to fixing environmental problems. About one in three farmers belong to a Landcare group.)

I have a different lot of land now, 'Sheep Camp', on a ridge of the Dividing Range, about twenty kilometres from Spring Farm as the crow flies.

Right to the end we said we would never leave Spring Farm. And so it seemed through all the eleven years we owned it, planting trees, running sheep, writing books, raising three daughters. Here I learned tree-planting habits. They started with water and the practicality of getting water to trees and keeping it up to them. Bucketing water to seedlings in a drought was a daily task.

There was an old Dangar Gedye piston pump near the power pole in the lucerne paddock, ten metres from the creek. I learned to dismantle it, to fit new leather buckets and gaskets, and to put it together again. I built the all-weather pump shed—the first structure I ever made with my own hands. It had to be done in three days to get county council approval and the power connected in time to be useful. The shed is still there today, loosening its roofing iron. I see myself down in the dark, summoned from bed, nails between my teeth, and wielding a hammer to stop a mad, wild flapping.

Contractors built a one-hundred-and-ten-thousand litre

concrete tank in the top paddock, eighty metres head above the creek and a kilometre away. It was finished on 12 December 1982, the date scratched in wet cement. Gravity-fed water plunged down the hill in a fat pipe, and then radiated out in narrower pipes down to eight millimetre spray lines. There was an old system of troughs and I connected watering lines to them, fencing-in tree plantations. Polypipe made it easy to be a bush plumber. The sandy soil made digging easy.

The kitchen table was always covered with tree catalogues from bulk suppliers. They were inevitably Victorian. Lucas Farm Trees in the Dandenongs was the main enticer, with a new wonder-tree in vogue each year—paulownia, matsudana willows, hybrid cypress. (If I come back in another life and want to go into business it will be as a farm tree supplier, a purveyor of dreams.) We tried many, but had best results with what we found ourselves through local knowledge. The Tablelands of New South Wales have frosts of such severity that they defied the credibility of early explorers. The enemies of seedlings are frost, wind, poor soil, rainfall, insect attack, stock damage. Trial and error remains the rule, down to spots a few metres from each other.

My mother, on the phone from Rockhampton, talked about the sandy soil at Drik Drik. Spring Farm had the same sort of soil, the same bracken, the same almost instant flush of green after rain, the same equally rapid drying-off, and also the same promise of trees to be grown in sandy soil as long as there was water. When the trees got their roots down to the water table—and they were the right trees—there would be no stopping them.

I kept thinking about where I would plant a small forest of

timber trees. Hovering around in my head was the thought of my grandfather. His plantings. My plantings.

I met two foresters. The first was Lawley Burrows, a West Country Englishman who grew pines and poplars near the Shoalhaven River. As soon as he realised I was interested in trees he sent his offsider, Graham McGrath, over to Spring Farm with a truckload of poplars and the free labour to plant them. We chose a boggy spring area near the cattle yards. There was a circle of stones on the ground and it was not until a decade later, when the spindly poplar cuttings were grown into stocky, vigorous-trunked trees, that I realised the stones marked a well, and I spent a week digging it out. I went down into the earth and down into the last century, when teams of itinerant well-sinkers travelled the country-side, lining shafts with tight-fitting stones.

Lawley Burrows was excitable, sharp-tongued, infectious with information about trees, and had the Johnny Appleseed quality of planting trees whenever he could. Later I learned that this was the mark of true foresters: they were not re-stricted to log counting, but threw their enthusiasms into planting. There is a row of poplars alongside the Braidwood sewerage works on the Bombay Road, planted around the same time as mine. They were Lawley's. I recognised his South American clones in other places. I saw some in the Colo Valley once, north-west of Sydney, and remembered Lawley had been there.

He wasn't in Braidwood much longer. He had followed trees earlier in his life, from country to country, and he returned to England following trees again. Graham McGrath came and did another job for us: he put a fence around seven acres of rocky hill above the house. We called it Conservation Hill and kept stock out. It was a great picnic spot, with a boulder the size of a house offering views down through trees to the creek, with bare paddocks sweeping away across neighbours' land towards the Shoalhaven River. A lot of talking was done there at those rocks. I loved making fires in the stones in winter, reading a book, boiling the billy, inhaling leaf-smoke, dreaming and having the dream at the same time. Judith Wright came one day and made a declaration: 'This would have been an important place.' She meant in Aboriginal lore. After a year or so the hill name evolved to Conversation Hill.

The second forester I met was Wilf Crane. He was my mentor and inspiration with trees, and so important to me that I wish I could remember when I first met him, and so record my initial impressions, because Wilf isn't around any more to compare notes. But in my memory he is already in the full flight of planting, explaining something about trees and, when finding that words weren't enough, throwing his arms in the air, grabbing a spade and starting on a demonstration.

Wilf worked for the CSIRO in Canberra, in the Forest Industries Division. Among his professional interests were agroforestry, research for a Super Tree, and projects investigating the cycling of sewage effluent through tree plantations. He was a soil biochemist and traced boron deficiency as a widespread common problem. He made tree guards and grow-tubes and was open to every conceivable way of giving a tree a good start in life. He was a mover in Greening Australia. The fullest expression of himself was to be out planting in the rain. When people talked about 'making things hard for a tree', depriving them of nutrition to 'toughen them up', he asked if they would do it to a child. Wilf had interests in forests at both ends of the Braidwood district, pines at Tallaganda with colleagues including Phil Cheney, chestnuts at Sassafras, and whenever possible he called at Spring Farm on the way through. He drove an old Holden station wagon, and sometimes an ancient Land Rover—vehicles loaded with spades, sacks, knapsack sprays, seedlings. He developed the Sylvaspade for Boral and had a presentation model ready for the 1988 Bicentenary. He started me on chestnuts. He found strong varieties of pine seedlings, and we worked out where to plant them. He sent his son, Andrew, to help me put them in. We planted four thousand. There was too much restriction in ground-travel for Wilf Crane and he acquired two small planes, a Volksplane one-seater and a four-seater Grumman Lynx. He flew around the countryside attending to trees.

Trees on farms grow from a word being spoken. I took that word from Wilf Crane: 'Let's do it.' It was as though through friendship with Wilf a hand swept over the acreage and a developing treescape materialised.

I wish there had been longer. But there's never enough time in life or with trees, and letting go is part of what a tree planter does. Practicality was Wilf's motto. 'You can do everything one hundred percent right with trees,' he would laugh, 'and still go ninety percent wrong.' All trees were his poetry, but chestnuts in particular. Trees and flight. He died at Bungendore in 1992, when his Volksplane fell out of the sky.

*

We sold the farm to the Sydney Water Board at the end of the same year. It will form part of an environmental exclusion zone if a projected dam is built. Meanwhile the house is rented and the land is grazed by a neighbouring farmer. The chestnut plantation is there and I want to go back to it when I can, to look at its bareness in winter. I want to be witness to its fuller growth at some time in the future, if the trees haven't been mauled by agisted cattle and if they have survived the marauding of sheep. I want to be there when their leaf-heads burst with green, and form a canopy in the sheltered zone below Conversation Hill.

I am not so sure about the thousands of pines. They were to be my superannuation policy. I had no doubt I would move through the plantation in future years busy with thinning, pruning, and applying a few principles my grandfather might have applied. I was going to use a forester as my guide, but it won't happen that way either. It is not part of the concern of Sydney Water, the new owners, whose charge is to have land in their possession once the final decision is made to build the Welcome Reef Dam on the Shoalhaven River. They have most of the land they need, now, and the rest awaits a political decision. When that happens and the dam is built the high-water mark will creep up Durran Durra Creek and flood the lucerne paddock. The pump shed will go under. The house will be demolished, if any part of it still remains.

I wonder if anyone will tend my trees, or if they will just grow wild and tangled across the former paddocks. Or if, as in an ancient forest, a degree of self-regulation will prevail, and it will be as if the human hand played no part in the organisation of the place.

# LIFE OF A TREE
# PLANTER

'Anything was possible now except the reeling
in of time . . .'

How it happened this time was different from the ways it might have happened before, but when it came, we knew this: it was always coming. The way he grabbed a spade from my hand, and raced up the hillside knocking thistles from the ground and levering up phalaris tussocks, it was coming then; it was coming in the jumble of gear in the back of the station wagon; in the way he wouldn't stop planting trees, even in the dark, especially if it was raining; it was coming in the worn teeth of the pruning saw; in the rattle of the chain saw; in the dribbling herbicide spray; in the dynamite demonstrations from way back; in the not quite out of control paddock of burning tussocks (in the joy of the flames). It was coming in the next beer and the next red wine and the next beefsteak at the campfire; in the sixteen-room bunkhouse he tendered for, ludicrously low, and won, and the expense it was going to be to have it transported away (at least thirty thousand dollars); it was coming in the expandable ninety percent (or was it one hundred percent?) special mortgage he'd got onto, and the beauty of it was, apart from being able to draw on it at any time, if you used up all your credit, you could go and have your land re-valued, and the mortgage limit would increase proportionately; it was coming in the way he always registered his vehicles in another state (if they were registered at all); it was coming in the accelerated growth of the Super Tree, that promised to blow itself out of the ground, a tribute to controlled nutrition; it was coming at the end of phase one of the effluent irrigation project, in the moment of self-sustaining growth when the canopy closed over, meaning that nutrients would have to be pumped somewhere else, because the plantation would have a life of its own then, and there would be no way out of the cycle except to move on to other trees.

It was coming in the closure of every circle and the completion of every meaning in life; it was coming in the slogan he coined for Greening Australia, *Think trees, Grow trees*, it was implicit there—because the tree was the symbol he chose early for himself, and made into a life for himself.

And it was coming in the two aeroplanes he owned, one touchy to fly, the other underpowered for what he wanted it to do; and in the fact that he loved both of them. It was coming in the flight across Bass Strait when I asked him if he wore his life jacket, and he said that Colleen had had hers on, but he didn't wear his, but kept it handy. It was coming on the day he took off at Sassafras and hit the fence at the end of the strip, ruining the propeller and wrecking the wings, and shaking him to the heart, as if, he said, he'd been betrayed by someone he loved. It was coming when the air traffic controller walked into the aero club and saw him sitting in an easy chair, and said, 'So you're the guy who's been flying the new regulations for the past year before they came in.'

It was coming in the idea of flight as spiritual leap; in the idea of tree as spiritual growth; it was coming in the image of flight and tree combined—in the image of the stumpy red Grumman Lynx taking off from Moorabbin and seeking a way over the Great Dividing Range back to Canberra, its pilot peering over the edge of sleep—over the lip of twenty-four hours in each day, never enough of them—but always getting through, tracking the cliffs of cloud, diverting to Mangalore, flying up over the Murray, following roads at times under low scud, and eventually coming gently down, safely down and certainly down as a settling leaf.

It was coming that night when Reg Ffrench watched the TV news, and saw what looked like the plane on the ground, the one that had circled The Elms at eleven-thirty that morning, the pilot hanging from the straps, waving happily. It was him. Accident. One person killed. It had come to him.

There was no way of putting off the news, asking it to go elsewhere. The word came like a known door slamming shut on a shadow. I saw his face. It turned dark in the expression of the word. I saw him leaning back against that door, on the other side of wherever he was. I saw his eyes ringed with tiredness, the shine of his brown eyes, the wild, wiry unsmoothed eyebrows, the kindly half-smile, the dropped shoulder, the voice about to speak, but not speaking, the voice about to say, but not saying. This was the moment when a man is revealed as a spiritual being, when the meaning shoots back through his life, and we know the insufficiencies and wasteful untruths of our own lives in the

waning light of another's, the moment of impossible trans-
formation, of mighty surge as we try to become immortal. I
saw the dirt under his fingernails from the planting of his last
tree; I saw the blue, stained joggers he'd left by the cooking
fire; the saggy trousers, the flannel shirt turning pale in the
final obliteration of choice.

I heard him explaining why Norwegians survive in the cold
better than other people, because of a trick they have with
otherwise unburnable logs, of keeping a triangle of wood
apart in proportion. (He knelt on the ground and described
this with his hands. 'A mate and I are patenting firedogs to do
just this.') I saw him lift a carburettor from the floor of the
old Holden, and tell me about getting a conversion to LPG
for free, through an interest-free loan from Boral, conditional
on using a minimum of three hundred litres a month (which,
he laughingly swore, he would easily). I heard him suggest in
a month when all the farmers were shooting their sheep
because they couldn't be sold, that each sheep carcass should
get its own post-hole, and a tree be planted alongside it, and
so what was wasted would cause increase.

I heard his voice at one in the morning: 'I've rolled the car.
It's back about four k's from the end of the bitumen. I've
walked a fair way trying every farmhouse along the way, and
now I have these lovely people out of bed, they're making me
toast and tea, could you come and give us a hand, Alec has a
winch on his Toyota, and we'll have the car righted in no time.'

He came tapping on a window pane, in the pitch dark, out
there among the spiky oleanders, frightening people as if they
had seen a ghost, and making friends for life in the moment
(though they would never see him again).

I remember that night—and the strange shower of rain at the road junction where I farewelled him in his righted Holden, asking him if the car (fully loaded), that had got such a jolt as it mounted a bank and came down thump on its side, was roadworthy for the home journey. Was he, who seemed dizzy-drunk from a blow, or shock, okay? He shook his head at the irrelevance of such a question; it had been fumes from a leaky jerry can that had made his attention wander, he said; he needed to be back in Canberra by dawn, there was a spit roast he was putting on for some people, a friend who had done him a kindness one time. The momentum of the man distorted the conventional run of hours, it twisted ways of seeing in the way of a work of art. He was the one who did things for others. He hurled himself at them being helpful. He charged himself up with caffeine and went on. When I got back to the last gate, returning after the car-winching, a vast silvery sphere materialised over the eastern ranges, like a magnesium flare, and I couldn't conceive what it was. It was morning.

Now he is on track from The Elms to Bungendore. Reg has farewelled him. The beautiful small plane with its pilot sitting happily above the wings recedes to a dot, shadowing over the shaley, wombat-riddled gullies of the Tallaganda forest. There is nothing untoward. It is a natural day. It is peaceful on the ground, with Christmas beetles helicoptering into the leaf masses of trees that are like planet spheres in themselves. Reg is back in his shed, pulling down his welding mask, joining metal to metal, fixing truck bodies, making gates, and mending the treads of the dozer that cleared the strip at Tagfor, enabling hair-raising take-offs.

In the sky something is wrong. What is happening in this flight? We need to get angry about this and ask what it is, raise our voices and shout until he hears us in the sky—because time has already begun altering for him up there, and for us down here, and he is parting like a splintering limb in a tree whose growth is not finished yet, and nobody has noticed anything yet. Not even, we have to guess, the doctor at his last flight medical—unless he scorned it, somehow, leaping that obstacle as he leapt so many others, by deciding it wasn't there. (Anything was possible now except the reeling in of time.) From here on in there could be no more connection between us, no more handshake, phone call, beer, mud map, field day, enthusiastic outing or celebration at Smiggins, Tallaganda, Sassafras, or Spring Farm, no more tree planting, gift of a sucker, bucket of fertiliser or two-litre jug of boron supplement left in a grass patch by the roadside for pickup later.

He flies under a bright sky into a darkening tunnel of pain. There is little time. He lands at Bungendore, in the paddock with a windsock and neat white ground markers. This unattended place (and places like it) are the paradises of wandering pilots, of which poetic company he is one. We cannot linger as he looks around, looking for what—a vehicle? A helping hand? There is a wonderful doctor in the town just minutes away by car, why can't someone do something about this? We can only accompany the darkening of his day brutally, with contempt for the images we create to hold him, now, the pictures of never wanting him to fall, of cycles, of inevitabilities and shared patterns and all the echoes of reverie that language breeds and nurses. This is no place for reverie. What we want is a mayday call from the paddock, an ear splitting yell, where he swings the prop looking white as a ghost, and clambers in for take-off, and there's never a burp or interruption to the smooth rumble of the Volksplane as she climbs, levels off, and looks pretty well trimmed and on track for Canberra.

Where is the hand-held radio, is it out of order? Can we tap him on the shoulder, and say if he feels unwell to get this plane down, shoehorn it in to a side street in front of the doctor's there. Come on, you can do it, it's your style. There is no flight plan, things happen in wild order. Everything stumbles and stops in the narrative of his progress at this point. It is a massive heart attack. The flow of words I am creating around him like a swirl of leaves in a gust of wind is gone. He is gone.

There are things anyone would want him to see and smell. I hope there is a fire somewhere, and the smoke is in his nostrils at the last, making him feel happy; and looking down, I want him to see down through trees.

# BUSH GARDENER

'Plant six trees for every one taken out . . .'

Tom Wyatt uses shredded newspapers as mulch. He gets the papers from the corner store over the road from Wyatt's Nursery at Kinka Beach, just north of the Tropic of Capricorn. Wet, the shredded newspapers bed down like wads of spaghetti. Soon they are grey-black as certain soils, and in garden beds insects convert them to humus. In a mango orchard at the back, Wyatt dumps loads of the Brisbane *Courier Mail* and the Rockhampton *Morning Bulletin* under the trees. Also colour magazines. They look as if they have been spilt from a trailer and kicked around. This is an experiment. Wild pigs have rooted through them. (He's had dogs in to deal with those.)

Tom is amazed at the wastage of paper in this country. He's putting it back into the soil, where it will become trees again. He doesn't know, at this point, whether printers' ink and the chemicals in the paper are going to suit his purposes. He could probably find out, in the sense that someone could tell him, but he's not about to ask anyone, not about to dig through research findings and discover whatever it is that scientists reckon. Tom Wyatt is trying this for himself, and then he will know. He's noticed that when his mangoes ripen the flying foxes don't attack them the way they do other people's. The reason is that his blackbutts come into flower at the same time, and flying foxes prefer blackbutt blossom to ripe mangoes. More people should note that. In another aside, he says that bees don't like mango flowers. He doesn't know why. If he comes back to life in another form, he muses, maybe it will be as a bee. Then he'll know.

As he talks, he pulls weeds from pots holding palm seedlings, leaving a trail of intense green stalks on the black plastic weed-mat of his nursery. In different parts of the nursery (open weekends only) his wife and some of the six children are at work. Tom calls it the farm down there. The June sun burns through the shadecloth. Tom doesn't seem like a high-speed weeder, but the work gets done quickly. Weeding is the root of this matter, the point of origin, the base ceremony of planting. If you won't weed, you're not a gardener.

Tom Wyatt is a tall, lean, dusty-pale man with a direct, hyperactive manner. He is fifty years old, with alert observant eyes and thinning hair that was once red. He looks like an earthmoving contractor or a mining engineer—a man accustomed to altering the landscape. Watching him work, flicking aside nettles and nut grass, it's emphatic that weeding is the first principle of horticulture and he's back to first principles all the time.

The everyday word for horticulture is gardening. Not a very grand word to some ears, but a good one in Tom Wyatt's. In the towns along the north Queensland coast gardening was the job councils gave to workers who were ageing, burnt out. A lot of people thought of it as a pension. There might have been the vestige of an old idea, too, that only servants were gardeners. You weren't fully yourself if you were a gardener. You were somebody else's person. Well, Tom Wyatt has no problems with the word gardener. The thing is to change people's view on words they don't like.

Nothing in gardening follows without the tiny action of selection, a finger and thumb clearing space for a forest. Tom Wyatt doesn't use herbicides or chemical sprays on the farm. He gets down there and pulls the weeds himself. He believes it's a mistake to try and create an environment convenient for human beings. There is no balance in that view, he says— banishing bugs, pushing everything away, creating pristine shelters without recognition of where we belong. 'Organics is ecology in action.' That's his motto. He applies the rule to himself, his own body. Life isn't something going on some- where else. It happens inside individuals, and as far as personal health is concerned, 'our antibodies need a boxing lesson'.


In the 1950s, as a boy in the Gulf Country, Tom Wyatt leaned from the saddle and looked at flowers and plants rather than following the other riders on the muster. His older brothers thought he was strange even then. They were all in the same world of rocks and dust and cattle, moving through the hot, open scrub from various agreed starting points, heading for the holding yards. When they gazed around, Tom was trying to add to the experience. He loved the life—throwing sticks on the campfire—boiling the billy—watching the stars—saddling up at dawn in the dry smell of the grass clearings. In the full heat of day he knew nothing better than to follow a creek downstream, to where it came to a waterfall. And it was like a rule. There would come a break in the trees, sky ahead, a wheeling of birdlife, ducks, geese, pelicans, finches in the shadows, hawks above, fish, tortoises, freshwater crocs nosing through the shallows—the life of the north crowding in to water from the glare of the open plain. Near the drop, creekwater that seemed hardly to be moving was streaked on the surface with lines of force, eddies, whorls and question marks, and then with a glassy edge sliding over—and so everything was broken up, changed. Water tipped into space, plunged into pools creating a snappy, quickly disappearing foam. There were waterlilies in those pools. Barramundi. Leaf matter turning dark, cleansing the flow. A continuous shade. Doves making the sound of coolness.


Tom Wyatt's father was born in Kent, and came out to Australia in 1923 as a boy of seventeen on a farm assistance scheme. He took to packhorse travelling and prospecting. His mother came from a station in the Gulf. Tom's father went to war with the Second AIF, was wounded at El Alamein and repatriated back to Australia. Tom was born at Mareeba in 1946, the youngest of six, and did most of his growing up at Charters Towers, among the bare and baking rocks of a tropical mining town—an unlikely place, you might think, for market gardening. But grapes and tomatoes grew there in the winter months, and vegetables thrived in a rich alluvial soil. Tom's father disappeared for intervals of six months at a time, seeking gold. It was the life for Tom as a boy: chores from pre-dawn until after dark, milking the goats, digging the ground, harvesting the produce. And heading off into the bush whenever he could. He was meant to work on a cattle property—that was his dream—always to get back to the bush. Tom's father taught him to be an observer, to watch what the birds ate, to try things out on his own initiative, and to learn from experience rather than just by asking. Then at a certain point he told Tom about a horticultural apprenticeship in Townsville. It was advisable for a boy to get a trade. Tom said later, 'He pushed me into it. And when he saw what I'd done, I gave him the credit for it.'

*The sides of the hills are covered with trees, which grow separately, without underwood,* James Cook observed in 1770, as he crossed the Tropic of Capricorn into Keppel Bay, off Kinka Beach. Inland there was much smoke, indicating a quantity of people. Cook observed through his eyeglass that the farther country was hilly, yet *by no means of a pleasing aspect.* He deduced the presence of a considerable river.

Today, the foreground of James Cook's view is Wyatt's Nursery. There is a succession of basalt headlands and beaches fringed with casuarina and pandanus. The Keppel Bay coast is a landscape of mangroves and mudflats, cattle properties, pineapppple farms, and holiday houses. No softness, even at dusk. Paperbarks, tough survivors, in the lagoons behind the beach; picnic tables; traffic roundabouts; a creek with fishing boats sitting on the mud at low tide;

thin-leafed eucalypts; ironbarks and spotted gum, rhodes grass in the cuttings; a south-easterly making whitecaps. Nights thick with silence followed by bright, harsh days waiting for something to happen.

Conversation with Tom Wyatt goes non-stop while he weeds. He mentions a man who bought a ten-hectare block, bulldozed the standing trees including turpentine (a fine timber species), then came and asked advice about planting natives. 'They were natives you knocked down,' said Tom. The man said the ones he bulldozed were 'too ugly'. When *Bos indicus* (Brahman) cattle were introduced to Queensland, says Tom, graziers were told by Primary Industries they didn't need shade, so many of them jumped in and cleared all their trees. They liked having an excuse, even if they knew damned well that all living bodies need shade. 'Bloody pioneers' are still a breed in Queensland in the 1990s. Old timber-getters and sawmillers had an understanding and respect for the forest: 'Plant six trees for each one taken out.' But 'bloody pioneers'—they're still around.

The potential for growing trees in Australia is virtually untapped, says Tom. It amazes him. Australian imports of timber are worth more than our meat exports, yet we have the best hardwood in the world. We nail it up inside our houses and hide it from view. Recently he visited Clermont, inland, six hundred kilometres north-west of Rockhampton, and found the people there had planted vast numbers of trees on the floodplain dividing the town. They did it as a Bicentennial project in 1988. 'They didn't know why they planted it,' says Tom. But it doesn't matter. They've got it and it's thriving. A forest of mixed species.

At the rear of Wyatt's Nusery there are mosquitoes, burrs, beehives, lantana. Waist-high grass like whips of steel and the canopy of the mango trees almost closing over. It is a reminder to me of what it's like to be back in Queensland. An impression, in the hot shade, of time suspended. You could spend your life there holding still. It would be endless and yet it would seem to be over in a moment. Why bother to do anything? I experience an impatience to get out, yet at the same time I want to surrender to what it can offer: to locate a piece of dirt, to build a board-floored tent screened off from insects, to plant trees.

By 1974, when he was twenty-eight, Tom Wyatt had risen to second in charge of Parks and Gardens in Townsville and knew that when the top job came round he wouldn't get it. It would go to an outsider because it always did. So he applied for the job of Director of Parks and Gardens in Rockhampton. His boss wrote him a favourable reference, but was appalled. There was a famous botanical gardens in Rockhampton, more than a hundred years old, but Rocky, said the boss, as everyone knew, was stifling, bare, hemmed in from sea breezes by those Berserker hills. It wasn't like Townsville, open to the breezes of the Coral Sea. It was a place so hot that people took blankets with them when they went to hell. Tom Wyatt shrugged and said, well, if he didn't like Rockhampton he'd come back to Townsville and take the top job. He'd be an outsider by then.

Over twenty years later Tom Wyatt is still finding things to do in Rockhampton. A photograph taken from high over the bare shining galvanised roofs of the city in 1974, compared with one taken from the same position in 1996, shows the change: bush rolling down from the hills, shade filling the bare corridors of this Queensland town—it shows something like the creation of an urban forest with street trees and parkland plantings—a process inseparable from the person of Tom Wyatt, who came in person from the bush to the city.

One of his first projects was to propagate six thousand bottlebrushes and plant them free of charge. The night they went in, two thousand were ripped from the ground by resentful householders. Later when they saw how the bottlebrushes improved their streets they asked for replacement plantings. Parks and Gardens agreed. 'Don't worry about the lemons. Make more lemonade,' became another motto on Tom Wyatt's lips.

Each year the Rockhampton Parks and Gardens nursery propagates thirty thousand trees. One-third are lost to vandalism and natural death. The rest survive planting out.

Recently a Victorian couple moved to Rockhampton, attracted by 'heritage trees'. Those particular trees had been growing for only seventeen years. Tom Wyatt had planted them.

The office of the Director is a modern glass-walled building buried among trees, just down from the Fern House in the old Botanic Gardens. The scope of the Director's responsibilities are wide. When I arrive to see him one morning he is on the phone deciding what to do about the desecration of the statue of a Brahman bull that stands in the Bruce

Highway median strip on the southern entrance to the city. Someone has attacked the bull with a hammer, smashing its balls. To whoever he is talking on the phone the Director calls them *testes*. The perpetrator he calls a *vandal*. Official exasperation is mixed with personal high spirits in Tom Wyatt's voice: how is he ever going to catch this miscreant? It's always the same twit. *Mix razor blades in the plaster of Paris*, he mutters from the corner of his mouth when he clunks down the phone.

The phone keeps ringing. A trainload of sleepers is ready for inspection. No time today. Interview with this writer. Meetings with mayor, prisons chief, and speech to East Rockhampton Rotary club. Young female office assistant wants his advice on something.

'Think for yourself,' shouts Tom. 'What would you do if I had a heart attack?'

'Jump on your chest, I'm trained in cardiac arrest.'

'You wouldn't have a hope. My chest is like a steel plate.'

Coffs Harbour is on the phone—what do they want? They want to come up and see what he's doing. Fine. Great. Rocky is the best part of Australia. We ought to secede, cut loose, sail away. Come on up. Now what—people in Rudd Street want to move a tree? On the desk is an emu egg, a 'No Bull Shit' coaster (barred like an anti-smoking sign), and a sticker with the message: 'Organics = ecology in action.'

'No-one in local government wants anything that's sensitive,' says Tom Wyatt about all the things that keep coming at him from every side. 'So they give it to the Parks Department.'

I want to ask Tom Wyatt if he ever finds time to sit back and rest in the shade of a tree. But the question doesn't occur.

There's no time for it, and the idea of his tree gets lost in his trees, plural. Tom's on the move, jawing. He talks about bringing the bush to the city. Says this often. He's done it already but it's not enough. The way he tilts back in his chair suggests the way a bushman props himself on a stump. The bush is in charge. The idea keeps regenerating inside him. He's already out there under a tree in his mannerisms. There's a belief in the air—as if trees have a quality of making inner changes in people. 'City people are anti-tree. Trees change the way people live in towns. We're making changes.'

It is impossible to separate trees from people's attitudes about themselves—their fears, their lack of self-acceptance, their timidity and their ignorance. But nothing is inflexible in human response. People can live and grow just as trees do, they can struggle and they can overcome what is in themselves. In Rockhampton, what was it that made people anti-tree? One thing is continuation of the pioneering spirit: a tree is there to be cut down. 'Bloody pioneers.' Well, that has gone too far, and the reaction needs to be fed back the other way. Tom Wyatt is feeding it back.

# THE RED BULL

'Such trees as he and his descendants planted showed
the desire in a new country for imprinting the values
of the old . . .'

THE QUIET man bought a bulldozer and started clearing around his house. It was a big house like something from *Wuthering Heights* but in Australia. This wasn't the sort of clearing that left a landscape torn and desolate, ready for the plough. It was delicate, personal, attentive work he did on those clunking caterpillar treads—edging the cold, heavy blade between trunks of old trees and plucking overgrown, dead and dying Monterey and Canary pines and setting them down in heaps. Around he went with this mechanised trowel. It was weeding on a big scale, a job (with time off from sheep-farming several thousand acres) that took a couple of years. He left other old trees intact although he didn't like them much—the Himalayan cypress, the photinia, the arbutus or Irish strawberry. It was a mix of growth common to old gardens in the Monaro, but some varieties were uncommon enough to make the garden at Cambalong noted for its rarities—trees and shrubs that would once have been planted on Indian hill stations. So here was an image of Scotland twice removed to the cool high country of south-eastern

Australia, in a wide grassy valley at six hundred and fifty metres. From a hill above the house the wild profile of the Snowy Mountains was visible one hundred kilometres to the north-west. Captain Ronald Campbell, a Loch Tay Scot who in 1831 first settled 'Bombalo' (later, when the town took that name, the property was renamed Cambalong) was ex-Indian army. Such trees as he and his descendants planted showed the desire in a new country for imprinting the values of the old. Robert Campbell comes along to reverse that trend, with reasons of his own that are like an expressive self-portrait.

The pines had grown shaggy and stark over more than a century, towering over the house, plunging it into dank shadows. When Robert and his English wife Henny took up residence in the late 1970s the homestead had been empty for twenty years. Now there were three daughters running through its many echoing rooms. The pines Robert attacked with his bulldozer were the other side of an argument he was having with the landscape. Here was a young family needing an expansive place to grow, not a place turned in on itself.

A couple of years previously Robert had planted four gum trees in front of the house, *Eucalyptus viminalis*, ribbon gums. They were the first of a large number he planned to put in, slender with pale creamy trunks and grey curling bark, pleasing to the eye and suited to the landscape. Up in the high gullies and ridges above Cambalong fantastic, shapely old ribbon gums had survived sheep and cattle. There were forest casuarinas there too, hardy as old iron left gnarled and isolated on the ridgelines. Many of them would have been growing before white settlement. There was a saying about native trees in Bombala—where clear-felling of native forests in the mountains towards the coast had left tens of thousands of hectares looking like the battlefields of the Somme—'if you planted any new ones you were a greenie'. What was a greenie anyway? It was hard to tell. Someone 'different', that was for sure. Someone who wasn't from Bombala. So where did Robert Campbell fit in?

He put a greenie sticker on his car.

Robert Campbell was born and raised at Bombala. His father gave him his first rifle at the age of six. He did correspondence school supervised by his mother. Whenever there was anything interesting happening on the property he was allowed to drop whatever he was doing and get involved. The things that fascinated him most were graders and bulldozers. At the age of twelve he experienced the shock-troop initiation of boarding school. Tudor House at Moss Vale was regimented but Cranbook in Sydney was better. His father had been there in the 1920s and gave Robert hints on how to get out of work. After leaving school he worked the property with his father and on the side started a trucking company. In his early twenties he hauled timber from the state forests around Bombala until his experience of forests laid waste by clear-felling sickened him. He did a lot of driving getting his work done, organising trucks and drivers, and keeping up with a social life. He liked good cars, he liked driving fast. When he went before a magistrate for a second speeding ticket in a short space of time he found himself in trouble. He was given three months' imprisonment. *Gaol? Just for speeding?* It was unthinkable. An appeal went before a judge. The judge was inflexible. The appeal went against him. Three months it was. Young men of good family had to be shown an example.

In Goulburn Gaol the screws told Robert Campbell they thought he shouldn't be in there for such a trivial offence, but when they saw his drivers coming to see him and discussing trucking company business they were resentful, and they locked him in maximum security. Robert Campbell will tell you it wasn't such a bad experience for someone who'd been at boarding school—living among hardened criminals—that it was much the same. These were grown men who meant what they said. They looked you in the eye and you knew where you stood. They, too, in certain circumstances, you might imagine (if, say, they lived in Bombala), would have had the defiance to put a greenie sticker on their cars.

In the cold air of the Monaro a red bull makes its way down a dusty hillside and crashes through a fence. Inside that fence is a garden planted more than a century ago. Dense shaggy pines and deciduous specimens formerly choking each other to death are tangled in windrows after the passage of the bulldozer blade. The red bull makes its way almost delicately through the mess, an invader from the drought-stricken paddocks. Riding the skies behind him are flocks of white cockatoos, five thousand and more wheeling and screeching.

Branches scrape muscled shoulders and scratch dribble-streaked, rough pink nostrils. The bull has something in mind. Between old buildings he comes on, trotting and swishing his tail, crashing past the weatherboard station-hands' cottages and the neglected stables, past the old-time cooks' rooms and maids' quarters, and along the high granite walls of the homestead until he stops.

He stands on a square of lawn. At the far side of the lawn, delicate in the cold light, are four high-country trees, *Eucalyptus viminalis*, ribbon gums, in front of the homestead where carriages used to draw up and early motor cars disgorged their travel-sick loads from Cooma. They are the first plantings inside the garden of species native to the landscape. The bull seems to have them in mind. Anyway that is the direction he is headed.

# TREES WITHOUT NAMES

'The tree's solitary unhappiness took on beauty and almost sang, or at least cried out . . .'

YEARS AGO the painter Tom Carment went to Zimbabwe and was so overwhelmed by the roaring spectacle of Victoria Falls that he turned his back on the boiling river and drew only one picture, a dung beetle struggling along a path.

Tom liked neglected places, unloved places, patches of earth the rest of us turned our backs on. In Australia he returned to them often—tangled bushland near West Head intersected by saltwater inlets; a bare paddock at Bombala dusted with frost; flat saltbush country under the Middleback ranges near Whyalla; a sandy patch of burned-over grasstrees near Perth; and to Sydney's eastern suburbs cemeteries, where in the boisterous southerlies hardly anything grew that didn't struggle, except where growth lurked in damp crevices fertilised by bones.

A lone Monterey pine grew in Botany Cemetery, in an industrialised part of the city near the airport—a coarse-trunked, badly lopped skeleton with a dangerous lean above jumbled headstones. Nobody cared for it much. Cemetery workers cut the tree back and muttered graveside warnings about limbs falling on mourners. It appeared stalky in various lights—limbs snapped off—bleak in the blustery marine light of nearby Botany Bay, desperately sombre in the thick, rust-coloured haze of polluted mornings as container trucks roared past.

It was a tree marked for the chainsaw and Tom came to watch the light gather around it in skeins. A depressing tree, he admitted—which was why he liked it, he said, shrugging off my questions, not really having answers beyond what alerted his eye.

Months later, on gallery walls, images of the tree above those tilted headstones gave a sense of a lost forest's last remnant. The tree's solitary unhappiness took on beauty and almost sang, or at least cried out.

Tom painted at ground level with his brushes and pencils, the canvas flat on the dirt and his neck aching from looking up. Staying on to catch dark effects he was sometimes benighted after a painting day, feeling his way home along barbed wire fences, clambering up rocky gullies. Carrying his work he delicately negotiated his steps to stop the wet panel brushing foliage. Once he fell and found himself sprawled, dazed, unable to move for fifteen minutes or so, wondering if that was his end. Even in daylight sometimes he got lost walking home. The bush was like that, in Australia, bewildering. Getting lost was a theme in colonial painters' work as they struggled to claim strangeness. It was still what painters did. Early mornings found Tom going out in an old army greatcoat with the frost on his back, setting up to watch a particular tree declare itself in the dawn fog.

When Tom found a place that felt right, a tree or a thicket

of trees, he prowled around for up to half an hour like a dog deciding where to sit. At West Head scarred, burnt, anarchic processes of growth filled his workspace. There was hardly ever any green—just bushfire-scorched blacks, ant-reds, subdued silvers, dappled greys. Grabbing a handful of fresh charcoal after the bushfire had been through he drew with the material of the subject itself.

But then, months after the fires were gone, green exploded —so many small new shoots sprouting from charred trunks that the bud colour took on a massed effect, thickening the nature of light itself as if through a prism—green tinged with growth-tip red. Some time later still, after rain and another summer, Tom returned to where the fires had been and looked for the tree he'd painted time and again. The tree was lost in regrowth. It had shadowed onto his canvas and then grown back into the mass of trunks and branches where he once found it.

Tom squatted on a rocky bank overlooking dappled-green, sandy-bottomed salt water. He insisted on going painting alone, with no-one to distract him from the urgent rush of work. (To recapture what he did we sat in a darkened basement room with a slide projector humming.) The thin-trunked trees in the foreground cut the frame into strips and intensified the wateriness beyond them. It was light coming through the trees as much as the trees themselves that drew him.

I wondered if trees to a painter were comparable with how they were in botany—solidified sunlight through the growth-engine of photosynthesis—a texture of light made three-dimensionally weighty. Was a painter of trees returning trees to the light they came from? Enhancing the gift? Was imagination praise? Was it what was meant by prayer, except secularised within understandable limits?

Tom never cared about the names of trees, never minded how trees were otherwise defined, what their botanical names were, or why they grew where they grew, or how. He remembered Krishnamurti's guiding idea from the age of eighteen, when he first read it: 'When you name something you think you've seen it.' The light around the trees he painted had an emotional content, he said, and that was what it was for him.

It was interesting. He could no more give a name to that emotional content than he could give a name to the trees.

# SIGNS FOR THE GATE

'Conditions for catastrophic fire come right about every
five years . . .'

THE FIRE gate was open and the country ablaze. Australian trees were packed with volatile oils and the harsh, wind-blown summers desiccated crowns and roots. Sailors coming up the east coast observed the ridges hazed in smoky blue light and incessant twinkling fires at night.

The British tradition of fire was to shut that gate and keep it locked. But a celebration of bonfires seemed to be always taking place. It was perfectly exasperating. The people of the land were figures in a charcoaled landscape carrying firesticks and moving through the bush seemingly intent on wilful pyromania. Such use of fire was derided at best as profligacy, at worst as carelessness. There were better stewards of the country coming in, or at least so they claimed.

With Aborigines denied their land the bush grew back to announce the wisdom of the burn. Trees thickened almost impenetrably between Sydney and the Blue Mountains within twenty-five years of settlement. Within another generation it was forgotten how naturally inviting to grazing the south-east countryside had been to the British eye, with its few great trees per acre (each one charred up the trunk) and native grasses flourishing under the soft pads of the kangaroo. The incessant cultivation of the country by fire over perhaps sixty thousand years was denied, underrated. But as herds of sheep and rough bark huts multiplied the word bushfire entered the vocabulary of Australian English as a cry of alarm. Conflagrations of immense destruction began —nothing like those creeping, scurrying, licking fires of the indigenous fire-farmers in their regularly burnt-over country now changed and thickened up.

A well-grown forest unburnt for years was an explosion waiting to happen. Three centimetres of leaf-litter was equivalent to one centimetre of refined gasoline lying on the forest floor. The more securely the fire gate was locked the more dangerous things were. Fire descended on farms, roads, towns and cities with a raging red tongue. 'Once torched, the burning bush resembled a spiral nebula, its fuels and fires like paired arms locked into an accelerating vortex.'

Settlers learned the rough art of burning off, getting rid of the fuel in the cooler months before it turned lethal, but it wasn't until the second half the twentieth century that the science of Australian fire developed.

Fire needed a guiding hand to open the fire gate and let fire back through.

Little in the story of the fire scientist Phil Cheney's early years suggests fire in his future except one day a column of smoke appeared behind the family house at Newhaven, on Phillip Island, Victoria. This was in the early 1950s.

The grassfire burnt into a scrubby area farther back and Phil watched from the beach as a group of locals put it out. 'It scared the hell out of me,' he recalls. The cause of the fire was unknown at the time, as far as Phil knew, but recently he discovered—around fifty years after the event—that he'd 'copped the blame'.

Now that Phil Cheney is Chief Bushfire Research Scientist at the CSIRO in Canberra the story feels like a reversal of cause and effect. Surely the man who knows as much about bushfires as anyone living in this country of fires must have fire embedded in his psyche?

'I don't think so,' smiles Phil, eyes narrowed to slits as if from peering perpetually through smoke. 'No more than anyone else in the Australia of the time, at least.'

He recalls smoking out rabbits and bees, and once lighting an old banksia and the tree burning out of control as he bucketed water from the swamp, and then giving it away— standing back and watching the burning tree blazing all alone, isolated from the bush all around in a fiery display.

'It worried me as a kid,' he says.

Water seemed more likely than fire as an element to mark Phil Cheney's direction. His father was a fisherman, and from an early age Phil went out in the 'couta boats. His father was a 'couta fisherman—this was done by trolling hand lines from a twenty-five-foot open boat. As a summer job Phil moved onto cray and shark boats. 'This was real *Wake in Fright* stuff in the fifties,' he says. 'The boats were often a floating arsenal with .303s for shooting sharks or dolphins that were "scarring" the fish, and shotguns for shooting sea birds, some-times for cray bait but mostly to relieve the boredom between shooting longlines or setting cray pots.'

In fourth year at Wonthaggi High, Phil was given a blue-covered careers booklet, 'Taylor's Diary'. A Forestry Scholarship caught his eye for no special reason except he wanted to work outdoors and didn't want to go fishing, or go teaching, either, that almost inevitable career path for capable students from country high schools such as Wonthaggi. There was no particular love of trees, but a youthful hike across the Victorian Alps gave him a taste for bush life and forestry work was outdoors, he noted.

A couple of years later Phil matriculated from Yallourn High School (where the science teaching was better) and was working the cray boats in the summer vacation before university started. He was at sea on a trawler when his Forestry Scholarship interview came up, didn't know about the letter, but no matter, the Reader in Forestry at Melbourne University, John Chinner, drove down to Phillip Island, came down to the dock and sought him out. He was interviewed at the boat.

'I think they were short of candidates,' says Phil dryly.

Unpretentious, understated, practical hands-on philosophies in the Australian bush-worker tradition permeated the forester profession when Phil Cheney entered it. Scholarship holders were expected to work in the field when they weren't studying, ten weeks every summer. At the Australian Forestry School in Canberra, where Phil went in the early 1960s, his first job was working with Ron Grose, whose research focussed on the fire-dependent life cycle of *Eucalyptus delegatensis*, the Alpine ash, and ways to harness it in forestry. The Alpine ash is a large hardwood of the upland regions of Tasmania, eastern Victoria, and south-eastern New South

Wales. It is closely related to the Mountain ash (*E. regnans*), the tallest hardwood in the world.

Australia's eucalypts are adapted to fire but respond to fires of many different sorts, depending on the species (there are over six hundred species of eucalypt). Mountain ash is extremely fire-vulnerable but at the same time fire-reliant. The tree burns to destruction but seeds prolifically after fire with the result that forests of *regnans* are evenly aged. 'The fluffy ash accepts the falling seed, buries it, encases it in an environment full of mineralised biochemicals and temporarily purged of antagonistic microorganisms.'

Grose's research showed that cut forests wouldn't regenerate unless the slash left after felling was burnt beforehand. In this environment Phil Cheney received his fieldwork initiation— on hands and knees in a charred seedbed taking measurements, soil temperatures, and readings in weather stations. The forester as tree adventurer was a streak in both men.

'One day,' says Cheney, 'Ron and I were taking turns in cutting the top off this tree at twenty metres above the ground (the diameter was pretty big at this height). I got to a point when the tree started to crack and split down the stem. I had visions of being squashed flat against the tree by the safety harness so I came down. We waited hoping the wind would blow it off but it stayed there. If I recall correctly we tossed a coin to see who would go up and finish it off. Ron won so up he went (I'm sure he would have gone up if I'd won). Being a relatively short and thick spar it made a quick vibration that shook Ron violently—fortunately the split did not go any further.'

\*

For many years forestry students lit fires on Bruce Ridge, on the slopes of Black Mountain overlooking the older inner suburbs of Canberra. This was their fire-lighting exercise patch and there they had the freedom to learn about fire and the responsibilty drummed into them—as fuel smouldered at the end of the day—to stay overnight and guard the fire until they knew it was dead. 'The most reliable way to ensure that fuel is dead-out,' says Phil, 'is to feel it with bare hands.'

Such practical philosophies, derived from common sense experience, were reinforced from the lessons hammered home by Alan McArthur, the first full-time professional fire scientist in Australia and the man, now legendary, who became Phil Cheney's professional mentor in fire science (and Phil, after McArthur's death, his successor and advocate).

McArthur as lecturer in fire control ran the fire exercises for the students on Bruce Ridge and must have seen fire smouldering in Phil Cheney vocationally speaking. At the point Phil graduated and finished serving his three year bond it was somehow water again in Phil's mind, except he was without a work offer in the specialty he'd chosen, water catchment research. He was in fact in Sydney with his friend Wilf Crane looking for a yacht in which the two intended sailing around the world. But it wasn't to happen. Phil found himself press-ganged into forestry from a boat dock for the second time in his life—this time by Alan McArthur. He became his assistant.

It is obvious to anyone with long experience of fire—like McArthur and now Cheney—that the fire gate can't be held shut in Australia until too late. It has to be opened to let fire through before fire comes and reduces the gate to ash and goes on raging elsewhere. A succinct principle to hang on the gate: those who fail to use fire to fight fire will be destroyed by fire. Conditions for catastrophic fire come right about every five years in the fire crescent reaching past Adelaide, Melbourne, to Sydney and through the thickly forested Dividing Range areas of the hinterland and across into the expansive grasslands of the Riverina and western plains.

McArthur it seemed had fire in his psyche, a fire-lover's excitement over the phenomena of the blaze. It extended to herding fire like a stockman and running it down until it came, exhausted, to a stop. 'It can be done,' he said, 'and as long as you work systematically you can wear it down and beat it in the end.' His primary motivation was to make fire-fighting safer and pursuing that aim he was very strong on prescribed burning. Phil Cheney took up that crusade.

Anyone with a box of matches or a cigarette butt—or even a farm implement such as a rotary slasher on a hot day making sparks over rocky ground—can start a fire. 'Where a fire starts,' says Phil, 'is very much a matter of chance. With extreme weather conditions, how a fire starts is frequently unusual and often bizarre. Once ignited, however, the direction the fire will travel and the area it will burn are reasonably predictable.'

This is the point at which fire science research meets the situation of ordinary people caught unprepared or in the wrong place at the wrong time and speaks to firefighting units charged with fire control. Indeed, perhaps no area of Australian science speaks more directly into the most frightening and archetypal moments of our experience. The essence of fire control, Phil emphasises, is the local land-holder and the community bushfire brigade. 'In a severe fire season, grass fires must be attacked very soon after they start and while they are small. In a country like Australia this is done most efficiently by the landholders themselves. A fully professional fire service would be prohibitively expensive and could not, in any case, get to most fires as quickly as local people . . . Forest fires are more complicated and one has to consider more variables. One also has to have experience to put the importance of the critical variable for each particular situation into the right context. To the layman, what might seem important in one situation may not be so important in another.'

Fire science as developed by McArthur, Cheney and their colleagues spreads the net wide. It includes experimental fires at the height of the fire season, in both grassland and eucalypt forests; intensely detailed studies of Australia's worst fires' history (Black Friday 1939, Hobart 1967, and Ash Wednesday 1983 setting the benchmarks); and comprehensive studies of how fuel loads affect fire intensity. Phil Cheney's office issues a stream of technical papers on aspects of working with fire ranging from the combustion characteristics of innumerable Australian fuels (grasses, trees, leaf-litter, even sugar cane) to matters such as whether it is better to wear fireproof protective clothing or light cotton clothing when fighting a blaze (emphatic answer: the latter). Fire-danger rating tables first developed by McArthur have led to a circular slide rule (the CSIRO Fire Spread Meter) able to give readings within minutes in the field, allowing firefighters to predict rate and direction of spread, and now programs that allow firefighters to predict and map several hours of spread pattern of a fire on their laptop computers in a few minutes.

Getting years of research across to people in a few minutes is a skill few scientists have, or perhaps even need, whereas in fire science it is a matter of life or death.

'These days it is becoming more and more difficult for volunteers and landholders to get the experience. Farmers no longer use fire to clear their land and even stubble burning is becoming less common. The main users of fire in southern Australia have been forestry and their influence is diminishing under economic rationalisation and the trend towards plantations rather than regenerated native forest.

'The average citizen is becoming totally unfamiliar with fire. They don't have it in the hearth any more—even matches are replaced by gas lighters. I am concerned that our firefighters do not get enough practical training—particularly on high-intensity fires. It is the only occupation (apart from war maybe) where people can be thrown into a life threatening situation which is not only way beyond their experience and expertise but their practical training is with fires that are perhaps only one or two percent of the intensity they are expected to face. Governments need to spend much more on practical training and land managers, farmers and plantation owners need to provide training areas containing the levels of fuel that they want firefighters to work in. In the past only forestry workers gained this experience through prescribed burning for regeneration and fuel reduction.'

Picture Phil Cheney leaning over the farm gate getting his points across, casting those narrowed but watchful eyes around for the pile of tyres or the stack of timber that waits to feed the advancing fire that will surely come one day across the paddock and sweep towards the house and sheds, looking for fuel to spark, making embers to drive into the vulnerable spots that human nature stubbornly denies are a problem.

'The best way to convince someone they've got to clean up is to invite them to drop a match on the ground on a day of high fire danger—when there's no wind, though. They're usually surprised.'

Perhaps this is why McArthur chose Cheney, because of Phil's laconic affinity with people who know the land as he does himself—from the bush-worker and tree-planter per-spectives, the forester-perspective of one trained in an era when the connection between those who used the land and those who most vocally cared for the land was closer than it is now.

Every year in Australia people are caught in apparently inescapable situations and tragically burnt to death. People burnt saving their houses. In their cars. Firefighters on bush tracks finding no way back, none forward, and the tanker incinerated. Firefighters huddled on a slope on a day of no wind, in a season of low fire danger, trapped.

'It shouldn't happen,' says Phil. 'It needn't happen.'

I asked him if he was confident of getting out of any fire-danger situation facing him, even the most extreme.

'Yes—always.

'But,' he added, 'I read the signs earlier and get the hell out of there if I have to.'

# THE STORY OF ROSIE

'The only wood in the story of Rosie was coffin wood, but the tree was there in the reaching out of her life. Her journey wasn't finished, her story wasn't told all through . . .'

I was the cook, and what I noticed was that Rosie hardly ever ate anything. At breakfast she was never there, except at the last moment, grabbing a piece of cold toast or a lump of congealed egg and even then explaining it wasn't for her, it was for her friend, Louella, who needed looking after. Then she'd run from the shearers' quarters to the shed, five hundred metres and sometimes farther, getting there just in time to grab a broom at seven-thirty start and get started.

They said she was the best rouseabout that ever was, that singlehanded, picking up the fleeces, running them down to the classing table, women like Rosie had set an example to men in this country, who considered rousing a job for any old blow-in. Back in New Zealand they started as babies slung in baskets over the wool tables as their mothers worked. Here they lived wild. They were uprooted and it wasn't their place.

The times I tried conversation with Rosie she'd lower her eyes and make an escape. At twenty-nine she had a shearer ex-husband and two eight-year-old daughters back in New

Zealand being looked after by the family. She had a look about her that said this time in Australia wasn't her work time, it was her life time, her party time come what may. If anyone was telling her own story by the way she lived it was Rosie.

'The trouble with you Kiwis,' I heard an Australian woman once yell, 'is that you consider every fucking night party night, whereas us Aussies, we're more sensible, we just do it once a week, and otherwise we just have a few quiet ones before tea.'

Nights of sitting on the hot steps of inland huts passing round a joint, or gathering around a fire of pine offcuts in the drizzle down south, passing round the bottle. Bailey's Irish Cream was Rosie's favourite, she settled into it with Louella, a smooth, foamy, sweet romantic mixture with a green landscape on the label unlike the red rocky places around Broken Hill, where Rosie worked mostly.

One thing I heard Rosie say. Another I learned later. She said, 'I love this country, but I don't want to be buried here if I die here. I want my body taken home.' What I learned later was that she'd said she didn't want to live past thirty. The only wood in the story of Rosie was coffin wood, but the tree was there in the reaching out of her life.

Rosie fell in love with Calvin, a young man who was built like a shipping container, who shuffled when he walked, spoke hardly at all to anyone, and was nicknamed The Terminator. He was a slow worker, a learner, a member of the team through family obligation. Back home his uncle was a famous Maori orator. Rosie sat on Calvin's knee and ran her fingers through his hair; she picked clothes for him for the Night Train nightclub, togging him out in Country Road, the Beau Brummel of the pool table and the back lane punch up.

When I came back after a year Rosie had a baby, Rewa. Calvin was the father. People were amazed that a perfectly healthy child, with smoky brown skin and rose-petal lips had survived the rigours of Rosie's lifestyle. Rosie, it emerged, was a fine embroiderer; she had made all the shawls and bedcovers for Rewa herself. Calvin cradled Rewa on his forearms, trudging around the yard cooing and chuckling. In this yard in Broken Hill they had a hangi, the red hot stones sparkling in the dry air, the plain food cooked in the ground-oven drawing the mates in from all around before they dispersed again. Coming together and splitting apart was the pattern.

It must have been like this for Rosie: her journey wasn't finished, her story wasn't told all through—there were places still to go, sheds to be worked, parties to be played out, right down to the last lonely cassette on the ghetto blaster as the sun came up. Calvin meanwhile flipped his lid. He gained an impression that a pharmacist had something against his child because he demanded payment for a prescription before handing it over. So Calvin took the truck belonging to Harold, his teetotaller cousin and leader of the team, his pro-tector, and rammed the truck through the plate glass window of the pharmacy, then drove down to Victoria somewhere until he ran out of steam.

During the year Calvin spent in Bathurst Gaol, Rosie started living with another man, Bonzer. She didn't want a permanent arrangement but Bonzer did. They used to argue about it. I hadn't met Bonzer in the time I was cook, but I'd heard about him; he was one of the old team from Kiwi, one of the central personalities, a sweet man said the women, a good bloke said the men. When Calvin came out of gaol he used to follow Rosie and Bonzer around like a puppy dog.

What happened next in the pattern of those lives, which seemed to follow the pattern of the stars, needed an agent of change, a tragic instigator, and it seemed to me that when the time came for an explosion it would be Calvin who would play that part. But Harold became exasperated with Calvin's hopelessness. Station owners were saying they didn't want Calvin on their land. Harold took Calvin to the airport and the mates frog-marched him across the tarmac and onto the plane for the first leg of his ride back to New Zealand.

So it was just Bonzer and Rosie that day at the Silverton Hotel. A Saturday. Lots of drinking by midafternoon, culminating in an argument, a fight. She couldn't live with him and she couldn't live without him; what was he, dim not to understand? Rosie said there was no way she'd ride back into town with Bonzer, no, leave it, so she set off to walk, twenty-five kilometres, enraging Bonzer with her stubbornness. He set off after her, cruising past in his old Holden station wagon, and then farther up the road turning around, getting up speed, who knows what Bonzer was thinking, wipe her off the map, obliterate her argumentative strength, her power of having the last word, for everything that he, Bonzer lacked.

I heard the news on ABC radio the next day. Maori shearer kills de facto. A few hours later Harold rang, this was just

terrible, the worst thing in a life of travail. He described what
had happened, Rosie after she'd been dragged along under
the Holden. She was his best worker, his confidante, he
couldn't believe all this. 'You wouldn't think,' he sighed, 'that
a small woman like that would do so much damage to a
vehicle.' They were flying the body back to New Zealand,
Bonzer was in the lockup, no bail, he wanted to kill himself.
There was to be an autopsy at Glebe morgue, I was living at
Glebe, so here they all were a day later in Sydney. I met them
at the airport and brought them over to sort things out, two
house-filling uncles and Harold with two-year-old Rewa on
his knee, and a room at the Rooftop Motel that by the end of
the week would be sleeping six. Rewa kept looking around in
a dazed fashion for Rosie, who had taken her everywhere,
almost everywhere, and she tugged at Harold's knee and
called him 'Mum'.

I'd been a writer trying to fill a need, to match my own
barely understood story with the story of other lives, to claim
a wider story as my own. This was where I met the Kiwis
before I ever visited New Zealand. I'd been at shed cut-out
parties where photos were taken, addresses exchanged,
promises made to meet up again and never to forget the
family feeling that developed in those rough, tumbledown
places. When Rosie's scant belongings were dumped on the
living room floor and Harold started blithely sorting through
her diaries and photo albums, I saw what she'd been after, the
thing that made life so cheap, but so fierce. It was there in the
story she told about herself in photo after photo, in the
captions denoting friendship and wildness and calm reflective
standing to one side. From the back of the most recent album

an article I'd written fell out, with a photo I'd taken of Rosie sweeping with a plastic broom. It was a proud memento.

'When her body is taken back to the marai,' said Harold, 'people will get up and say what a wonderful person she was, then they will say that if she had never left New Zealand this wouldn't have happened, and then they'll blame me.' He pulled a long face. All things came around again and there was no escaping them. 'She was a Ratana,' said Harold when we went to the New Zealand High Commission and they asked her religion.

'What's that?' I asked.

'It's a Maori religion where people do whatever they like, they drink, swear, fornicate, and then they say their prayers like there's no tomorrow.' He shook his head in bewilderment. 'It doesn't make sense.'

# SECRETS OF
# TU BI-SHEVAT

'A tree could just as easily be a vine or an evolved grass such as wheat or lupins in the definition of the ceremony...'

WHATEVER THE season—and it was mostly dusty and hot up there, in the north-western corner of New South Wales—the orchardist Joe Joseph wore a dark blue suit and a frayed white shirt buttoned to the collar. His small, sharp-featured face (pointed like a bush mouse's under a cloth cap) was tanned, but with a jaundiced sheen underneath. On his feet instead of boots he wore leather sandals.

Joe's hands shook as he rolled a cigarette. They tremored selecting fruit from the tray of the old Dodge, pressing oranges, figs and grapes into the baskets of customers. When he came to the Anglican rectory—where my childhood friend Boyd Spackman lived—payment was waived unless the Spackmans chose to bless him with what they could afford. That was the way Joe expressed himself and did business. This was many years ago, of course.

Joe Joseph had war neurosis but rarely spoke of his experiences. While being marched across Europe, so people said, his band of fellow captives was bombed by the Allies, but with a wife and baby he made an escape. The Second World

War was an adventure in the minds of boys in the 1950s, and Joe's story of walking through a forest and meeting some Americans who gave them gum, which made them sick, seemed tame to Boyd Spackman; nothing compared with dogfights over the Channel and prisoner of war stunts.

After arriving in Sydney and staying in the migrant camp at Fairfield the Josephs had ventured as far inland as the railway line permitted—to our town of galvanised iron roofs baking in the sun. It was a place where even white kids, the least deprived, went to school barefooted, in hand-me-down clothes, with ringworm and rickets and other poverty illnesses. Everyone said that Joe had struck it lucky in coming there. Two miles out was a block of land with house and sheds standing empty beside the Darling River. Boyd was proud of that river, part of the longest inland waterway system in the world, where he went fishing for Murray cod, bird-nesting and chasing bog-eye lizards. But when Joe and his family saw the Darling they wept over a chain of muddy waterholes. Then Joe got to work.

He seemed too frail to be running an orchard, doing the work of digging, weeding and barrowing, picking and packing without the assistance of tractor or rotary hoe and with only limited seasonal labour. All he had was a draught horse left by the man who had abandoned the block before him, a rusty set of harrows, a hauling sledge consisting of ironbark stays and lengths of railway line for skids. There was also his daughter Leah to help.

She worked in the packing shed and around the house. Her mother had gone back to Sydney. The plan was that Leah would join her when she finished primary school while

Joe stayed on and sent money down. For Leah, aged ten, Sydney Girls' High was already picked out, the date set (a year off) when she would sit the selective exam, and even a career was chosen for her in the distant future—she would become a doctor.

Leah sat with Boyd in fifth class and although he strove to beat her in every kind of test except arithmetic (where he conceded defeat) she easily managed to sail past him. When the teacher placed the class against the back wall for spelling bees and general knowledge quizzes it was always Leah left standing alone at the end, after they'd battled it out over *committee, committed, their, there, they're,* and they'd fielded questions about the location and length of river systems and Australian primary products listed in order of importance. When it came to apple and pear exports the class gave a cheer and Leah gave a curtsy.

It was exquisitely humiliating for Boyd to be beaten by a girl who'd arrived in infants school barely able to speak English. If Leah faltered during a quiz, as she rarely did, there was a sympathetic groan. At the moment of victory the teacher took her by the armpits and swung her onto his desk, where she stood taking hurrahs with a confident grin. Everybody was in love with her, although speaking for myself I barely remember her, or even Joe Joseph for that matter—I was three classes below Boyd and it was like another generation down there in infants.

Whenever he could Boyd headed out along the river road to visit Leah, pelting along on his overlarge bicycle to make the most of daylight. In his memory there was usually nobody else, just him, though Leah had lots of friends. Our town had a rainfall of only six inches a year and in the months between intermittent storms the river road was rarely graded. Deep boggy ruts created by Joe's truck were baked into year-old trenches making bike riding hazardous. Sometimes Boyd got there grazed and bruised, covered in dust, and with flat tyres from the burrs that littered the track sharper than carpet tacks. Flats, difficult to mend, were Boyd's badges of devotion, in case Leah ever noticed. He remembered sitting on a fence post listening for the sound of the truck, his heart full and waiting for Leah and her father to return from the afternoon fruit run.

One morning before daylight Rev Spackman took Boyd to the railway station to see homing pigeons released from wicker baskets for a race back to Sydney. Joe and Leah were there, loading boxes of fruit into a freight carriage, pausing for a minute to watch the pigeons rise into the sky. Every variety of fruit imaginable, fresh, dried, and candied, was bedded on strips of newspaper and wrapped in yellow tissue paper. There were seasonal grapes and figs, but also other fruits including small, sweet and slightly leathery-skinned apples, melon-sized oranges, wrinkled olives packed in salt, lemons, walnuts, almonds, pears, quinces, cherries, and even pomegranates. The consignment was obviously intended for a special occasion and Rev Spackman raised an eyebrow when he saw the addressee in Sydney. It was a man he called—with a broad wink—his fraternal colleague.

Rev Spackman talked about Joe Joseph in affectionate but rather mysterious terms, said Boyd—using hints and circumlocutions as he did when talking about Masons or Roman Catholics. Eventually Boyd understood that Joe was a Jew and the 'fraternal colleague' a rabbi, the Jewish equivalent of a vicar. What Jews exactly meant to Boyd at that age he couldn't remember. He couldn't say what Jews exactly meant to his father either because he never asked him, but he believes his father saw Joe as something like a revered relic.

Boyd was particularly sensitive to his father's attitudes and experienced them in his imagination in a way that influenced his life. As one who'd found Old Testament Hebrew challenging at Moore Theological College, Rev Spackman would have admired Joe's facility in Hebrew script and Biblical lore, drilled since childhood in Poland. But because New Testament teaching painted Jews as forerunners of Christians in the same way as lungfish came before land mammals, a convinced Christian would have had no choice but to think that way too. Yet again, as a Low Church Anglican, Rev Spackman would have had the notion of the many paths to salvation.

Did his father understand, though—Boyd asked many years later, when we met and swapped life stories in Bill and Toni's café behind the Museum—that a Jew stayed a Jew whatever the misdeed, even if he denied his Jewishness? Even if he was an atheist? Christianity couldn't match that level of acceptance with its hoops of faith and belief to be jumped through. Boyd told me that even back then he had a niggling conviction that Christianity was a fraud thrust on the world, and that something else would suit him better. Something that wouldn't change the inner person whatever wind blew.

So in his twenties it happened that Boyd underwent conversion at a small synagogue near Sydney University, where he worked as the specimen collector in the Department of Zoology. Since then he'd written a PhD, gone to Arizona, and now worked at the Australian Museum in the reptile department, from which he was about to retire at sixty. He'd never married and outside his work led a life of study and prayer, keeping to the many obligations of Orthodox Judaism.

My amazement must have shown in my expression.

'Well, people do say that reptile people are very strange,' Boyd ruefully admitted.

When it came my turn to give a summary of several decades I took the short cut of encapsulating my life into a string of book titles. I ended by telling Boyd what I was writing at present—something I normally disliked doing, as it felt like having teeth pulled, and the people who seemed most ardently interested usually didn't read me anyway (as Boyd hadn't, with the excuse of Torah and sacred text commitments far into the night). But I owed Boyd something after the intensity of his memories, and there was another connection we had, namely that my second wife was Jewish, not all that observant but we inevitably celebrated the year's major festivals. To show I knew my onions I named all five of them.

Boyd leaned forward over the café table where we had just ordered our third espresso, and said there was another one too:

'It's an obscure one but might interest you. Put it in your book about trees. Ever heard of the trees' birthday?'

I hadn't, of course.

*

For many years, Boyd continued, he had almost forgotten an invitation he and his father received to visit Joe's orchard and join the Josephs, father and daughter, for a celebration supper concerning trees.

It must have been issued the morning of the pigeon race, he said, and they would have gone out there a day or two later. (By the following year Leah had left and Boyd never went out there again, to that bend of the river where glossy-leaved orange trees were varnished with sunlight on every leaf.) It was strange, though, considering his later life—Boyd certainly remembered visiting with his father but recalled nothing of the particular celebration beyond the cornucopia of produce on a side verandah table where, as usual, visitors were urged to take what they liked. He supposed they sat down and went through a certain routine but he couldn't remember a ritual, nor wine because he always remembered alcohol—the times when his father drank were engraved on his amazement. Over prayers and blessings, Boyd admitted, he would have switched off as he always did as a child. Perhaps he even ducked away from the table or buried his head in a comic. He would have had his attention on Leah, though, always there in the corner of the eye with her long black hair lustrously rich and tangled, and eyes that seemed to pick lazily through his mind.

Sometimes they just lay around in the shade and read or played intense games of snap with a tattered pack of cards—then out to the cool-shaded packing shed they'd run to fetch bridle and blinkers. Down to the riverbank next, where a haze of green showed as the water evaporated, and the old draught horse stood waiting in the puggy mud. The two of them (and at times, Boyd supposed, a maximum of the six of them, when there were others) jogged on horseback through the rows of orchard trees, so deeply shaded in that arid, bright landscape. Finally Boyd helped Leah in her chores—she was good at making happy slaves of her friends—and then it was time to go home.

Over the years various sayings of Rev Spackman came back to Boyd in fragments of mental static:

'The last razor blade in a packet lasts the longest.'

'A tube of toothpaste is infinite in quantity if carefully rolled.'

'Ants are always ready for trouble.' (Like his father, whenever Boyd saw an ant bed he grabbed a stick and annoyed the ants into a frenzy.)

Another saying Rev Spackman bequeathed to Boyd was:

'Trees, like racehorses, have a birthday on the same day—Old Testament tradition.'

Boyd couldn't date it, but surely the saying sprang not from the Bible but from the time of Rev Spackman's visit to Joe Joseph's orchard. In fact, he'd recently had it confirmed.


Boyd was in the dining room of a large, old-fashioned flat in Woollahra when he heard someone say:

'It falls on Tu Bi-Shevat, the fifteenth day of the month of Shevat—the New Year of Trees according to the Hebrew calendar.'

There was a woman in the room, a stranger to the group of friends gathered for the Passover Seder. She sat midway down the grand table.

'Oh, the trees' birthday!' she exclaimed.

The rabbi called attention to her.

'Does everyone know Leah?' he asked, placing his hands on the crown of a dark, glossy-haired head.

She was a tanned, elegant, fine-boned woman of around sixty who twisted with birdlike pleasure under his touch.

'Good Yontov, everyone.'

'Leah is one of my favourite people in the whole world,' said the rabbi. 'She's our guest from Adelaide.'

They all greeted her. When it came Boyd's turn he found himself blushing. He'd been Jewish for years, but always with an unworthy fear that somebody would jump up in synagogue or study group and expose him as a Christian fraud—saying it was only because of falling in love at the age of nine with a classmate who had led him, spirit-wise, he knew not where, that he wore his prayer shawl around his shoulders and dipped from the waist praying Friday night and Saturday sunset till his hips ached.

'Leah, I think I know you,' he said.

She stared, shook her head questioningly, smiled in a way Boyd remembered with excitement and then raised a hand to her lips in disbelief.

'The Comic Book Boy!' she said.

'I suppose so,' Boyd laughed, though he would have preferred a more impressive memory tag. They stood from the table and went around to greet each other. Leah took Boyd by the hands. He'd forgotten almost completely that other element of their friendship: comics. But now in his mind Boyd saw himself riding the river road with a stack on the handlebars, tied in string: *Superman, Captain Marvel Junior, Donald Duck* and *Girls' Own Stories*.

'You kept me endlessly supplied,' said Leah. 'I loved Superman's X-ray vision, and guess what happened?'

'You became a radiologist,' said Boyd, intuitively playing snap.

They went back to their places at the table, and the long evening marking the redemption of the Israelite slaves from Egypt proceeded. When it was over, Leah and Boyd sat up late.


My wife and I came to Boyd's celebration of trees near the beginning of the following year. Boyd had studied the ritual and led the service with Leah at his side. I can only give my impressions, but they were very strong—of two people completely at ease with each other, rich in humour and affection after one of them, Leah, had made a long roundabout journey through life (two marriages, both ended, and living on several continents over a distinguished career) and the other, Boyd, seeming to have in some sense always been arrowed straight for her heart.

Being there in the dining room of Boyd's narrow East Sydney terrace was like experiencing one of the produce displays I remembered from the Royal Easter Show. There were more than twenty varieties of fruit piled on four large boat-shaped platters. Locating much of it fresh at the wrong time of year was a tribute to Boyd's dedication and a reflection of Australia's climatic spread. We sat on cushions, a dozen of us packed in, the long, low plank table taking up the full length of the room. Boyd seemed to have gravitated to the Hassidic or mystical side of Judaism where a kind of rushed noisiness prevailed, bursts of song, prayer, and pithy phrases worthy of *Reader's Digest Quotable Quotes*. Some of his friends looked unusual—a couple of barrel-shaped men with beards dense and scrolled with room for birds' nests in them, and their melon-shaped wives in headscarves and wigs, and wearing plain print dresses to the wrist and ankle. That they were doctors and therapists was not immediately apparent.

The four platters of fruit were each eaten in sequence with a cup of wine (or more) as blessings were said. We began with bread (representing wheat), olives, dates and grapes. A tree could just as easily be a vine or an evolved grass such as wheat or lupins in the definition of the ceremony. The Seder for trees followed the same pattern as the Passover Seder but despite the theme being introspection and self-searching it had a wilder, more bacchanalian or primitive feel. Boyd had located a dozen superb shiraz grown in central Victoria that were blessed by a Melbourne rabbi as kosher, and I found myself getting a bit drunk, and I wasn't quaffing as much as others. The main text or theme Boyd used for the evening was a noisily argued one: 'For is the tree of the field a man?'

I expected closely argued analogies about this (based, say, on head, trunk, feet and roots, etc.) but not at all. It had more to do with the idea that God 'planted' a few just or righteous men in every generation and on these the merit of the world depended. They set an example through envy or admiration in the way that branches were grafted from good trees and from them many other good trees were generated.

Envy as a way to good had never occurred to me, but I liked the saying, thrown in my direction by a humorous

Boyd, that 'the envy of authors will multiply wisdom'. Then relating to Boyd's chosen life was a text from the Song of Songs as we munched on dates: 'This thy stature is like a palm tree'—interpreted as meaning the palm tree didn't bend or sway in the changing winds—and so too the Jewish people.

Something else discussed was the connection between planting and faith, as many small seeds in any sowing always rotted and the farmer needed faith waiting for them to sprout. The word *zera* (seed) was a pun for *ze-ra* (this is bad), since at first glance it appeared that seed rotted and nothing good would come of it.

We ate, drank, and recited from texts into the night.

The strangest ideas seemed the strongest. There were scientists and doctors in the room, children of Darwin and Freud, but more powerful than any theory of evolution or the material mind guiding their professional decisions was the vision of the four worlds. Each was represented by a category of fruit because the worlds fell down to the vegetative level after the sin of Adam. Only the world of Emanation remained in holiness. The next, Creation, contained the minimum of evil and so had the fruit that was eaten whole, skin, seeds, and all—figs, grapes, persimmon and apples. In the world of Formation, where evil was more prominent, fruits were eaten with the skin but the seed discarded—olives, peaches, dates and plums. The fourth world, of Action, was covered with evil, and so its fruit must be peeled to find the good within—oranges, pomegranates, walnuts, and almonds.

It amazed me, remembering barely anything about Joe Joseph, that here in East Sydney so many years after his death his orchard was present so strongly—completed, so to speak, as Leah and Boyd touched hands.

Leah remembered the candied fruit she had prepared and packed for her father. Being made of peel they showed that even the husk could be transformed into good. A plate of these was handed around last.

# THE PARK

'He felt white-hot inspired, elaborating a theory of his own
at last, the idea of the universal spiral on which could be
attached anything ever thought or any action ever taken,
whether individual or social, by man, beast, or god . . .'

THE IDEA came to Burton when he sat down to rest on a patch of grass on a walk he took every day from home to work. At first he called it the bright idea because really nothing he thought out for himself ever came to anything much and a voice inside his head mocked him.

It was the month of October when Sydney winds were gusty and fresh, when the sun already bit and burned. We, Burton's old friends and colleagues, worried about him. He talked in loudly stitched arguments admitting no interruption, then pale-faced and looking alarmed stalked off seeming to ring a small bell and direct non-existent traffic with a hyperactive arm.

Finding himself in the centre of Centennial Park's six hundred acres Burton lay on his side, drew up his knees, and watched grassblades bend at angles in the breeze. Each new shoot—there were thousands of them—leaned away from him with a kind of opposite attraction. They pointed towards a huge dark fig with inky shade and heavy branches. It was like the primal tree in a Buddhist pilgrimage, rooted into the navel of the earth. Burton's idea was simple: to climb that tree and hang his backpack there. That was all the idea was—just a whim. Yet it had a sensation of pulling him in, and the only force holding Burton back from starting his climb at that moment seemed to have been the question of what his backpack would contain. It would need to hold everything he was.


Home at his paint-peeling Paddo terrace Burton had visitors. Through the open top of Bruce Hubbard's blue 1970s convertible parked with two wheels up on the kerb came the sound of Leonard Cohen lyrics. Hubbard, an actor, was married to Burton's ex-wife Sophie, who was busy unpacking a basket of food on Burton's front porch among dry potted ferns and a doormat shedding fibre.

'Hurry up, babe!' called Hubbard, tipping his head back and regarding Burton blankly through reflective lenses. Sophie later rang me and said she was always a little afraid of Burton now.

But she touched his cheek and in her raspy, intent voice asked if everything was all right with him. 'Are you eating?'

Burton lofted a stray cat with the toe of his boot and peeled back the lid of a Tupperware container. Chick peas. They meant protein and fibre going back to student days, when we all shared a house. A body needed those things. Burton muttered a checklist of the requirements of the physical life while reminding Sophie that a small tin of tuna usually kept him going for a whole day.

\*

Burton's job was teaching the history of sociology at Sydney's leading university. It was an occupation rife with great ideas but precluding any new ones in the mind of Burton the explainer. He taught a timeline from Karl Marx to Clifford Geertz and back again via Emile Durkheim, Raymond Aron, and the curiously named Dennis H. Wrong. Like a snowstorm in a paperweight Burton's lectures were composed of almost identical material year by year with variance in where the emphasis fell. Lately Foucault was more in front than Freud, but that was all. Sociology was a play without plot, with a distant action in which the characters were representative individuals only. Curiously, it was all very much like Burton's life, in which meanings rose to a more representative plane as his wife left him, his children led other lives, and we, his friends, ceased phoning or at best attended his crises like undertakers impatient for termination. His letterbox overflowed with unpaid bills that were finally eaten by snails. Burton was left the corpse of himself seeking understanding.

Being a spectator to experience was all right professionally —it was Durkheim's founding definition of sociology, after all, that individuals were subject to social facts they couldn't recognise, and needed specialist interpreters—but in person Burton was Icarus falling. In the park watching children play, cricketers at their game, or cyclists whizzing around Grand Drive he felt the spiralling-in of existence. It was here somewhere near and fearfully dear that he would come home. He felt the power of a centre and he himself at that centre. Mentally into the backpack went a small tin of tuna and the book of Leonard Cohen lyrics with paintings by Henri

Matisse that Sophie had given him when she first brought Bruce Hubbard home as a family friend.

Walking was Burton's habit, heading south from Paddo through Centennial Park and thereafter through angles of shaded, handsome streets—always choosing those with over-hanging fig trees and interesting root patterns on low sand-stone cuttings. Mostly he took them in the same order, crossing to the other side of the road when a certain cracked pavement gave him permission, or a street sign such as 'Walker' or 'Shoebridge' gave him the pun of consent. Outside shops when he found himself blocked by delivery trucks he stopped. Instead of going around he waited like a blinkered horse as the beeper of the reversing vehicle sounded. Walking was somewhat exhausting and Burton looked careworn, unkempt and was on some days, lately, obviously unwashed. A Mr Bayeh at one corner store and a Mrs Wing at another noticed his routines and started coming out, handing Burton something from the pastry cabinet gratis, an apricot Danish or a slice of baklava which he took on the hoof, wolfing it down, discovering sugar to be a prime necessity of the life of the mind. Had they known he was no itinerant, but the one edu-cating their children to social inclusion they would have been dumbfounded. Going early the sun was on Burton's left cheek and returning it was on his left cheek again. When he told them that they nodded in kindness.

Walking gave a rhythm to Burton's thinking that carried over into his Tuesday and Thursday lectures. He was already down to part-time duties yet counted the reduction in his circumstances as merely a commentary on what was happening to him, as if it were an indicative phenomenon. There Burton stood in the lecture hall sweating and breathing hard, wearing the linen trousers, the fringed embroidered waistcoat and the beaded casbah cap he'd favoured since postgrad years. Hot from striding, his heart hammered as he gripped the lectern and shaped his material into pentameters that pulsed with his blood flow. He felt white-hot inspired, elaborating a theory of his own at last, the idea of the universal spiral on which could be attached anything ever thought or any action ever taken, whether individual or social, by man, beast, or god. Meantime Burton's students got up a petition to the head of department and demanded Burton's removal for lectures that were barely comprehensible. What excited Burton in his private self was the growth of his idea, the way it extended down into his veins for nourishment and, far from being a contemptible bright idea any more, it was a theory of everything awaiting ignition to unite.

I understood him as best I could. Thinking excitedly while lecturing it was apparently easy for Burton to be in two places at once, to lay out the four functional dimensions or problems in the structural-functionalism of Talcott Parsons, say, and compare them with the simpler and more attractive propositions of, for example, Vilfredo Pareto and the inescapabale circulation of elites. Mentally at the same time Burton remained with his left cheek to the earth watching fingers of wind trailing through grassblades and leading his eye to the inky shade of a spreading fig. He thought he had never been so brilliant and on top of himself. A panel of peers sat in.

Simple to state the bright idea in complete form to our old

friend and mentor, Professor Maurie Weinberg: he would hang his backpack in a tree and return the next day to find if it was still there. Once tested, inescapable, implications would follow. What a lost diamond the idea was, a chip of eternity shining.

'Backpack?' asked Weinberg querulously from under his wild eyebrows.

Burton thrust the tattered object across the professor's desk.

'This is all very well,' said Weinberg. 'But it's about your health, mate.'

'My health!'

Weinberg wasn't prepared for the energetic way Burton leapt from the chair, a grin of self-justification slitting his taut, narrow face, and almost joyfully held his left wrist with the fingers of his right hand timing his pulse.

'Feel it!' Burton triumphantly cried. And so Weinberg felt Burton's pulse rate, and yes, it was amazingly slow. 'Fit as a fiddle,' Burton cried, and indeed when the professor put his hand on his colleague's shoulder he felt muscular strength and hardness of a rare sort. All the interior tautness Burton had developed over the years seemed to have layered itself and flowed outwards developing him physically, while ordinary understanding retreated inside him to the smallness of a nut.

When Weinberg conveyed to Burton the results of a Senate sub-committee ruling, standing him down, he asked Burton to hand in his door swipe card and to sign forms settling a twelve month leave of absence. 'A monthly doctor's report,' suggested Weinberg, 'might be useful.' This was a false hope, of course, as Weinberg had already begun filling Burton's post and discussing pensioning-off requirements with Sophie, who told him about Burton attacking her Tupperware containers without re-heating them, sometimes spooning them up while they were still half frozen.

My understanding of our old friend was narrowing fast. Burton strode through Randwick side streets avoiding his usual zig-zag of careful routing. At his back I could feel his life rolling up like a carpet going into storage. Urgency and excitement shook from him in waves, evident in his loping jog, his wild arms, his jerky head movements. He climbed fences and short-cutted through yards. The idea waited for him at the park centre, surrounded by a kind of glimmering, fluttering edge. It was now something seen in the eye as much as caught in the mind.

And now it is evening, twilight, phantasmal, as I picture Burton climbing the old fig tree to string his backpack from a branch. He finds it remarkable the way the sights and sounds of the world spread under him, dissolving dividing lines without any mental consideration needed. His intention this first night has been to hang his pack and get home before dark. But the interest and fulfilment is extraordinary and he reclines on a great branch, one leg propped up loafingly as he absorbs the changes. A cone of light comes around through the trees and flounces across the grass, then leaps into adjoining trees, hovers, drops to the ground and exploratively shrinks away. After ten minutes it comes around again. The light shines from a small truck that circles the drive but finally loses interest. Burton sees figures carrying sacks walking purposefully through the dark and disappearing under trees, and he understands them as fellow spirits, outside theories and paradigms, as souls sifting their priorities in gifted splendour. Then he feels it is safe to get down. It is wonderful in the park at night walking through smells of dampness and hearing nightbirds splash in the ponds and shriek in the paperbark trees. Burton feels his footfalls rippling out through this fresh new world. A kind of rumbling border surrounds the acreage—the whole of the city generating conflict and interplay, burning electricity oblivious to the meaning of waste. Meantime from inside the park a bubble of peace rises into the clear, cool sky.

Burton is happy naming simple things as they make grabs for his attention. Leaf. Dog. Possum. Rat. Euphorically he dances on the damp asphalt until he reaches the Woollahra gates. There he turns back and looks in under the trees and smiles to himself remembering the contents of his pack. The book of Leonard Cohen lyrics, all old half-grasped feeling and melody. Nibbles of nuts. Keys. Money. Credit cards. He barely understands their function any more, except that by forfeiting them to the night he makes a bargain, and he is no longer ours.

# WILD MAN IN
# LANDSCAPE

'I started reciting "Deep Well", the lines where spirit
trees writhed in cool white limbs and budgerigar . . .'

I SEE the fettlers' train snaking through the sandhills. The iron tracks straighten, the train gathers speed entrancing a man who hangs from the rattling window frame going farther with each jump of the rails into his dream of Australia, with a sense of always returning.

He can't let go adjectives from his mind—the red-purpled land, the blood-deep desert—the red fire beetles winking from the firebox as day goes down and the train goes racing for the dark mountains across the desert floor.

Bearded figures, Italian prisoners of war, stand up from the rails and get out of the way. Ranked beside the train they call out greetings. The man leans out shouting, *Come sta!* And the blurred faces call back, *Bene! Bene!* And he looks back at them receding, filled with emotion at their shared exile and the way the desert receives them.

He leaves the railway camp making emotional farewells to the boozers and brawlers sharing his loneliness—getting away early in cold starlight, out to the road which recedes in perspective, and where the looped wires of the overland telegraph line are highlighted before the burnt-red coming day. His heart is raked by the cry of black cockatoos. He longs for words of barbarous beauty equivalent to the bird calls. A tall, strong-shouldered man with a mop of Shelleyan hair, eyes rolling like a confused stallion's, with a swaying gait, he was trained to the saddle in stock camps since boyhood and in boyhood was taken by the ringers in those camps and thrown on a blanket and raped.

Far north, he wakes in a shack on the banks of the Roper River, props himself on an elbow and lets morning light fill his head through gaps in the walls. Flame of blossom strikes him, crimson flowers of mistletoe falling like a woman's hair—but he asks, was ever woman as beautiful as this gum, standing with smooth white limbs against the pure opal sky?

At night the tree is a dark cloud and he listens to cicadas drumming. She is the girl of a scattered tribe, the dark cloud holding a secret of the land. She is one of the people he sees, and humbly bows to, his mortal vision so intense it would drag him into another state of being if he wasn't a human being and thus held like a spirit in a rock.

They are tall, long-haired visitors in their own country standing off and holding spears. He sees them from the windows of the workers' train; sees them in a wrecked homestead where they providentially find shelter from the wind, their campfire burning like a star at rest among ruins of the fallen stone. He wants to find his own country as they do when they come in and spread their mission blankets on the ground beneath the dark acacia and bauhinia trees, surrounded by children and dogs, carrying dilly-bags and bundles of possessions tied up in strips of some old coloured dress. He wants, and he longs, and he craves: but he cannot have what they have in smouldering ash and fume behind the trees, because the thin-grassed ridges of their land are their home wherever they camp, but can be his only in passing passion.

By the riverbank and around the lagoon his words are leaves from the paperbark trees falling on water. Words are his join between what is not, and what can never be. When sunlight enters his shack in the morning it falls across his bed in the pattern of fig and palm leaves. The sun, he says, won't grant him rest. His feelings tempt by becoming half mythological, appearing in recurrent shapes—birds, shadows, stars, fires, trees—exciting him and wrenching him into love which is always heightened, and gaining him a certain celebrity and notoriety when he comes down to Adelaide like a wild man, a snorting primitive, one who has got there before the rest. But never mind that.

As yet unapproachable hills rise out of the dawn. Anthills stand ever away in the scrub and the dry grass. Brumbies come out of the purple ranges and feed in the reeds of the billabong where Birwain mourned Nerida, dived in and was changed to reeds. Would that he could be changed to reeds and spears of reeds, he roars, that fringe the lilies opening far out among their floating leaves!

Everything he witnesses has a moment of perfection: the tea-tree petals slipping into his billy-can as he dips, and say, for example, a wondrous commingling of birdsong at dawn and the vague forms of trees filling the opening of his tent. One bird keeps singing, the rain of the rest ceases and the one voice of all sings purely on, but sings in ending. This never happens again, though he camps in the same place—

everything happens with such perfection and then is celebrated and then mourned. His verbs pierce, his nouns
hammer, his adverbs splash the brow, his adjectives pour their
red, vermilion, and their crimson flush. Look where it takes
him. All comes down to boots and shirts and hat flung on the
floor, telling their tale of jobs, unrest, and change.

But he makes a prayer: morning so beautiful that the
breathing trees spread their boughs against the moving sea in
adoration.

Then he is back in the siding shed transfixed by stars, and
the train comes with its blinding light. Nailed boots disturb
his meditation. Into the day with the birds talking into his
ears he goes, curlew, wagtail, lorikeet, thrush and wren his
outriders.

But mostly it's the budgerigars that he follows, those small
parrots no bigger than a newborn baby's fist, hundreds to a
flock, thousands, tens of thousands and then millions darkening the sky. They capture and mirror the torments of his
mind, the unfinished and seeking self-taught brain so elegiac
and overactive. They come in a flash, particled, as he sees
them, throated with a shrill fierce cry, writhing and deployed
in banners of bird-smoke and streaming into the grey mulga
scrub and then soaring as if from a blaze of fire. They come
into the trees at Deep Well, into the trees he calls spirit-trees
alive with birds clustering them—Deep Well where the
fettlers' car travelled towards the cool blue rising wave that
was the Ooraminna Range, where, choosing to be a fettler, he
worked to lay red gum sleepers, lined and spiked the rails
with adze and hammer, shovel and bar.

*

He was past sixty the time I met him. I was in my twenties. He was the poet, leonine, sitting with his big white dog and saying nothing; fidgety, self-conscious, bursting with ego and feigning indifference. I could see it in the way he breathed, held himself, and almost snorted with self-willed invisibility and frightened me with his self-importance.

I had heard he was foolish and made difficulties, lived in his feelings too much, exploded. But when I spoke to him he stood and opened his hands with ease and acceptance, slouched a little into the storytelling mode of the country as I struggled to say what his writing meant to me. I started reciting 'Deep Well', lines where the spirit trees writhed in cool white limbs and budgerigar, and it fell away into a mumble, I got the words wrong—but did it matter? As I spoke my praise he opened like a desert flower and uncrinkled a thousand curious petals.

# THE SEED

'Her dejection was so deep it became a style of wit, as when
she saw a beautiful tree as a living ghost of death . . .'

LYING AWAKE at night she heard the whistle of a train travelling north. It was wartime and the trains were shrouded, loaded with guns. Through a dream of orchards they made a disturbing animal cry.

She listened as the black frost closed in, the walls creaked, the fire making the only warmth. Outside there was southern weather blowing the trees all one way to her. The hard inquiring wind struck to the bone and whined division.

Except how hardy trees were in Australia, how suited to what was spiritually strange, how beautiful in their hidden statements! Low trees, blue-leaved and olive, on outcropping granite; a clean, lean, hungry country.

She came from a wealthy landowning family. Their holdings spread through two states with boundaries superimposed on a country of ghosts. The song was gone, the dance was secret with the dead dancers, the hunters were gone, the painted bodies a dream. That was how she saw it, passing through on horseback. Her grandfather had surprised a painted warrior standing at the edge of a forest. Just as far back was old

Dan spinning stories into a blanket against the winter.

The road beneath the giant original trees swept on and would not wait.

When she saw a First War soldier's farm a cruel blessing met her eyes. The soldier asked for nothing but the luck to live. But every attempt to cultivate was a silent scream. The ploughland vapoured with the dust of dreams.

That man was a dreamer and the land was poor. His eyes let the whole gold day pass in a stare, walking the turning furrow. The love she saw in him affected her, though. It was between a man with searching eyes and a woman whose body answered to his arms. It was between the passing light and the enduring earth.

She was half spirit already, but rooted in obdurate reality. A brand of failure and a brand of ecstasy shaped her alphabet. Standing in the night, she said, we are like a tree—every leaf a star.

When the dreaming soldier and his wife were gone the trees were still there. They held their arms up to the light.

Her pessimism was the humility of the seed. Beauty gilded her dismay. 'Come back to the kind flesh, to love and simple sight. Let us forget awhile that we create the night.' Soon enough we would turn to minerals, crumble to ash. It was a dour thought expressed at a time of birth and new life.

Her dejection was so deep it became a style of wit, as when she saw a beautiful tree as a living ghost of death.

I remember how she walked in old age. Not very far, riddled with too much knowledge of what she would find when she got there, yet stolidly hopeful—as if there was light remaining below the horizon, and if she could get a little closer she could bring it up once more with a disparaging sigh.

'Where's home, Ulysses? Cuckolded by lewd time he never found again the girl he sailed from, but at his fireside met the islands waiting, and died there, twice a stranger.'

After the war she was hauled back from those big statements, back to the cell, the protein, the biochemical chain of which she was part. God walked through all her ages, but here she was a young woman again, passionate and afraid. A child grew from the seed she held in her. She was the earth, the root, the stem, the link.

Life began in darkness; eternity beckoned with images born in darkness. It was a faith she expressed as darkness raged like fire, spilling out life that would one day crumble and be gone back into the leafless, tongueless realm of rebirth.

A tree grew from a rocky crevice. Out of the torn earth's mouth came the old cry of praise. So whatever the tree was, counted. Whatever the bird was, was perfect in the bird.

Poets were born with a stone in their hands, staring and listening until they died still holding it, leaving their words escaping it.

She was torn and beleaguered by people trying to turn her into the ways of other people. She longed to fuse her passions into one clear stone, and be simple to herself as the bird was to the bird.

The natural history of the earth sounded a deep gong against the vanity of existence, and she saw our faces drowning in the river. She held the invisible wand, and could not save us. To know us turned to death, and yet not save us. Only to cry to us and not to save us. Knowing that no-one but ourselves could save us—that was the wound, more than the wound anyone could deal her.

She moved through a countryside of ringbarked trees and bare hills scoured with erosion gullies. These were the hills her father stripped, crouched like shoulders naked and abandoned. She drank from the scant creeks and ate sour cherries from abandoned trees.

It was too painful and she dreamed of the wounded hills bandaged in snow. She willed her thoughts to stand like trees after the departure of the last leaf and the last bird.

Unexpectedly up through a wrecked landscape ran a boy with a rifle and a black dog running behind. His heart foretold a rainbow. The boy believed he could do anything, break branches, swim rivers, outstare spiders until the rain came down in mattocks. He caught the rainbow in his hands, hung it on his shoulder, and made his way home.

Whatever created the world would not change until time was done, the white-ant would love the tree, and the strangler-fig had a woman's arms.

After she named all the trees in the forest and gathered the flowers she still reached for the one truth from which they all grew. Getting a medical reprieve of some kind she rejoiced in the grey city streets, and said, you with your mask of false smiles, you smelling of facts and factories, you watch out. One crack in a wall can spread, one seed can grow.

On the track down from her house to the river she set marker pegs on a route where human footsteps would do least damage. Her visitors went carefully, feeling themselves accomplices in the devastation of the earth.

She walked along clutching a stick, striking the earth now

and again like a conductor just a moment behind the orchestra, or like a composer whose notes have assembled all in front of her.

# AT SHEEP CAMP

'Here were the essentials we carried with us to Sheep Camp from the storage room at Jeremy's farm, starting a new phase of life . . .'

buckets, gas bottles, Esky, air mattresses, camp stool, easy chair.

*Cook house:* Four tin mugs, cutlery, dish tub and drainer, camp oven, frying pan, peg and griddle, triangle, toaster/griller, one large water drum (40 litres), one small water drum (20 litres), one large billy, one small billy, sieve, food safe (hanging), two toasting forks.

Remember how each simple item unpacked had an aura? How the toasting forks with their scorched wooden handles and bent prongs demanded their own lovingly fashioned hooks to hang by the fire?

One day there would be a house there on the saddle. When the house was built the discomforts and make-do's of camping would be gone. Talking about the house made the camping sweeter.

Then we took everything away again down the hill. The drive back was without the magic of coming in. Gates closed, tracks winding out; where was the excitement? Better to be always arriving, anticipating. Departure was demolition. Except, there we were, a few hours later in Goulburn, elbows jostling around the table, wedged in the Paragon Café eating fish and chips and drinking pots of hot black tea—celebrating, already remembering through layers of experience such details as red gum tips on the skyline at sunset flaring like a roadworker's scarlet jacket.

Next time, I made a writing camp—dashed down the

freeway to arrive at Sheep Camp before sunset, three hundred kilometres in three and a half hours. In steady wind I worked like Charlie Chaplin, doing alone what needed a helper and leaning against the wind to hold collapsing tent poles until everything sprang right and I rewarded myself with a Scotch by lamplight.

I had twelve days to 'break the back of that book'. Sleep was profounder than oceans. Next morning I walked around in a daze, feeling over-lucky, supremely privileged, and couldn't get started. Funereal cockatoos came from the high, cool forest at my back, languorously flapping and seeming to lurch and slide through the air. They were a sign, a gift, and I remembered waiting months at Spring Farm before the black ones appeared, and when they did (tearing into the stone pines) I felt a tension rise away. That was twenty years ago. Where did the feeling come from and why? It was the same sensation when gang-gangs came out of the cold and worked their way through hawthorn bushes along Durran Durra Creek. On the gang-gangs went, fluffed and scarlet-grey, nutcracker-beaked, doubled over like fists and hanging half upside-down gorging berries. One bird penetrated too far and crucified itself on the thorns, wings spread wide. Too late for any help, I found the bird mummified that windy, freezing August. Meanwhile out in the open paddocks galahs moved through the dry grass gathering seed, busy and oblivious—pink-waistcoated, grey-jacketed aldermen murmuring in undertones—and the world played a hard, bright, brass-band tune.

At Sheep Camp gifts came raining down. Gang-gangs and funereal cockatoos were common. Each morning the high forests disgorged birds in various strung-out flights heading for a day's foraging in the farmland below. From the highest paddock I could locate Spring Farm through binoculars, but only faintly, a line of poplars away out on the plateau twenty-five kilometres away. Maybe some of the birds reached there, where a full life had once been lived, when it seemed there would never be anywhere else, nobody else.

All those years ago I read the lines, 'We weep for our strangeness,' and stored the feeling without knowing why.


Arranged my writing table; ran a lead to the car battery for the laptop; opened my notes and weighted them down with a stone. Definition of writing: easy postponements and contrived delays infinitely multiplied. Went up the hill and looked down at the tent on the saddle. Sunlight exploded under trees and isolated their shapes distinctly in the land-scape. There was a purple haze from eucalyptus growth-tips over the forests. The tent, in cubes of green, tan, silver, was the ghost of a house or the prediction of a house. It had a blue tarp for a verandah awning and a silver tarp for the workroom floor. I half closed my eyes and multiplied its roofline. The tent was hot in the afternoons, even on cool days. Too soon for a house here yet, but the idea of a caravan beckoned, as if the house, like a seed unbuckling, would have stages of growth and each one to be gone through.

Seed pods of blackwoods crackled in the heat. The still, grey heads of yellow box trees thinned in the sun as I walked down the track to where I knew of a native cherry, half-hidden on a tangled slope—*Exocarpus cupressiformis*, a parasite, from which I took strength. The purple trunk of pitted armour was like iron. Turning from there I climbed through a straggly stand of half dead trees choked by mistletoe, a parasite also. The spare beauty of the mistletoe flower was like a tree-frog's finger pads, faint coral pink on toughened stems.

Then back up the hill to my work table. My diary records:

'Slow going with the book again. It feels too "spiritual". Need to roughen the boy stuff a bit. Got to have people leaping from the page and don't have it yet. Take from life. Just get it down.'

Looking up from the page I was connected through every dry crunch of leaves, each bird call, every flap of canvas to my boyhood self. Went and stirred the fire, boiled the billy. Made myself drunk on tea, bread and honey, like a grub-crazed tree-creeper. There I sat sniffing woodsmoke at the far end of longing. I was able to say to that boy, myself, far back at the beginning of longing, 'You will arrive and be grateful.' Gratitude was the overwhelming feeling of the person of faith—Susie found the quote—and I came into that gifted state just then, incoherently offering thanks to the light, to the moment, to the racing cloud-shadows, to the trees. I gave thanks to the flourishing parasites who gained their nutrition come what may, and whatever was needed in the writing came as I opened the letters and diaries of strangers, and streamed with invention.

\*

'Completely renovated. Suit artist,' ran the ad. So we bought the old caravan and persuaded a tow-truck driver to haul it to Braidwood the next morning. We spoke by mobile phone and I accelerated onto the freeway expecting to sight the convoy close to Sydney, but it took until near the Bundanoon exit, well on the way, before there it was, sashaying along ahead, a louche hippy leftover painted in grey-blue cloud shapes, matching speed with the growling yellow tow-truck as if a propellant was lit under its swaying tail.

The renovations included a double mattress on milk crates and all the plastic caravan fittings ripped out and replaced with cheap wooden shelves. A sink cupboard was painted with a macaw. Angels were daubed on the ceiling. The curtains were tattered, dyed homespun, embroidered with spiders and a name plaintively stitched: 'Greg'. We could hear lorikeets at evening alighting on the tin-clad skylights with a click of claws. At dawn it was two below zero inside, last night's cocoa dregs embroidered with ice-spears.

That first cold stayover we lay in bed with the round face of the gas heater ('do not use in caravans or boats') disking a red glow and roaring like a banshee. Firetail finches, *Emblema belum*, threaded the thornbushes at the back window. In the stand of ribbon gums nearby—where I watched, spellbound, the changes of light—shards of fallen bark crackled in the cold. How to describe that grove and make it eternal? The creamed aluminium smoothness of the trunks, the feathery, motionless leaf-heads where wire-thin twigs snapped and helicoptered down to be gathered for fire starters.

\*

We came again, and then again. And then one day we came in a mood of doubt and fear seeking resolution.

No easy words for this, except Susie wrote:

'I can't quite reconcile the softness, the round loveliness, the nurturing lovingness of the breast as host to this mutant, fearful, despised murderous abnormality. Nature is full of it, of course, plants, animals, insects of perfect exquisite God-given beauty that poison, strangle, kill. Parasites that invade have to be hacked out in order to preserve life for the host. My life versus its . . . Chemotherapy is poison, but the farmer destroys to grow. Think of the surgeon as farmer, tilling the land to clean it up. Radiation is natural. Rays free-float throughout the cosmos. Extant everywhere, that in therapy are mechanically focused by a machine. Find an image to use during treatment. Visualise the rays emitting from the palms of Raphael, the Healing Angel.'

Winter mornings. Close to three thousand feet we are above the deepest freezing fogs. Everything still and white, with a fuzzy sun coming through. Melodious conversation of a family of choughs using low branches like stepladders to overvault each other and spread out searching for grubs. At breakfast the sun melts the frost. But away below, the Braidwood plateau remains quilted with fog that folds into the lower gullies and holds the frost down there until late morning, sometimes past noon. The school buses rumble along with their headlights dully burning. The iron bolts on the stock and station agent's doors have to be kicked open in the cold.

What is there to do then except laugh with the beauty of the day, get the fire started, and talk about tree plantings and house plans?

# AT AKE AKE

'The vision seriously intends to stay . . .'

AKE AKE was a cattle-damaged, weed-cleft eleven acres running down to a shingly beach choked in gorse and wild tobacco. It also happened to be one of the most beautiful places on earth. When we first started going there together we didn't call the place anything

Flying across from Australia each summer we camped on a ridge of kikuyu grass where our tent overlooked the shining gulf. The moon rose above stacked islands in soft marine light. There was a crumbling cliff, a high headland where a sea eagle circled, and a feeling of land running out to the sky. The hill facing the campsite had an almost conical shape and Susie had called it Kiwi Hill because of an unusual soft feather she found there. On one side lay Omaru Bay, a shallow, semi-circular, flounder-fishing haunt. On the other was a wide sea-passage between islands. Yachts moored under Kiwi Hill depending on the weather, sometimes as many as eighty but they were hidden and all we heard was the clatter of their rigging and floating music from parties at night. When the sun shone, and it was hot, the sea broke into glass splinters.

When cloud darkened, the passage went leaden grey, motionless before a coming squall. The water was scrolled by tide currents and the wakes of boats heading for shelter.

The day came when we chose the name Ake Ake, meaning 'forever'. Nobody had that assurance of course. Forever beautiful and forever lasting? Forever to be used? Forever to be loved and repaired?

W.H. Auden wrote:

The winds must come from somewhere when they blow,
There must be reasons why the leaves decay;
Time will say nothing but I told you so.

Perhaps the roses really want to grow,
The vision seriously intends to stay;
If I could tell you I would let you know.

We called it Ake Ake as an assurance or promise against the realities that symbols shine through.

The ake ake tree (*Dodonaea viscosa*) resembled a tough shrub in its juvenile form and became a handsome small tree when grown. It survived on the clifftop among gorse, old pines, and twisted pohutukawa trees surrounded by a red debris of flower stamens. Ake ake timber was the hardest wood known, fashioned into war clubs and made into axle staves and even ball bearings, according to New Zealand bush lore. It had gently ascending branches and sticky branchlets. The kidney-shaped seed capsules were thin, papery and pearlised. When the seeds were ripe the ake ake rustled in the breeze like a snare drum hidden in the undergrowth.

Susie had been given the land by her father in the 1970s. Her sisters sold their portions but she held on. Before we met she thought about returning from Australia to live there, and asked Rob Morton, an island tree grower, how many trees would be practical to put in. Rob answered that around four thousand would be a good start.

When I heard that number I liked the sound of it, having once known someone on a treeless two thousand acres declare that a planting of ten trees, maximum, was enough. The definition of a tree planter I always thought was someone with a forest in their imagination and the where-withal to make the gesture with a spade. Such a simple choice but with an intricate connection awaiting. There was also the matter of having the land—good fortune, of course—but then with tree planting in mind there would always be acreage somewhere.

So they'd put them in, fencing out cattle from the beach and closing gaps in the remnant bush in the hope of shading out gorse, the dominant problem weed. Gorse had been brought from England by early settlers for hedge planting. They prized it as a solution to fencing problems on New Zealand's precipitous hills, stealing it from each other and swimming frozen rivers at night with rootlings clenched between their teeth in the hope of getting it struck.

Susie kept giving me lessons in how to look at New Zealand trees but I was a recalcitrant pupil. Except for kauri, manuka and cordyline the names were new to me—kai-hikatea, puriri, pohutukawa, nikau, totara, kowhai, whau. What did they signify? I had trouble separating shades of green. Even in a forest fully grown, with ferns crowning the upper branches of ancient trees, a great spectacle, I held something back from my admiration. New Zealand had none of the hardness I loved in Australia. Everything I defined in negatives through an aesthetic of opposites. I was an open sclerophyll woodland sort of person, I boasted, a lover of blazing sharpness where light spilled like acid and the nostrils clogged with dust or stung with bushfire smoke. Long-bladed reeds didn't cut the hands in New Zealand and thorns didn't snag. Kids ran barefoot through long grass—no snakes or bindi-eyes. My moods were attuned to bleary haze, purple distances, drought years and down-hanging leaf shades of eucalyptus, acacia, casuarina—silver, grey-green and earth-red. Nondescriptness secreting beauty and a subtle, immense variety were the sights on which I was weaned. I fixed on the drying grasses on the opposite islands with a stubborn home-sickness and mistrusted easy attraction.

Rob Morton had a philosophy of planting that wouldn't work in thin Australian soils. It was to plant in grass, and not clear the grass away, but use it as shelter. Not all the trees thus planted survived but most flourished. Seventeen kauris were put in but only two lived. Down on the beach a planting of pohutukawas disappeared. Up at the gate, on the ridgeline where the wind blew from four points of the compass, cabbage trees shot straight as rulers and flax thrived with emblematic profusion out of kikuyu grass that was matted, twisted like wire, and feet deep.

It was amazing how a planting of four thousand and a good percentage of them surviving absorbed itself into the acreage. On the cone of Kiwi Hill and down the northern fenceline, across the cleared head of the gully in 'islands' and then down the gully itself to the beach the new plantings darkened and thickened—took hold. On annual visits we struggled through and did counts. Getting down to the beach was an ever more difficult scrub-bash as weeds encroached into gaps, vines frothed over treetops.

Meantime more than half the land was still unplanted but that half was a no-go zone more than ever, gorse-ridden and thick with tobacco weed, a species that grew into a tree and had wide, soft, dinner-plate sized leaves and smooth amber berries the size of glass eyes. It was noxious to humans, although not, apparently, to a lurking dope grower who macheted a way in and spread superphosphate from plastic bags lugged through dim tunnels of thorn. The haul was harvested before we ever knew it was there. A well-motivated weeder, he would have been employable in friendlier circumstances, for none of his crop was left, everything cleaned out—the tattered archaeology of plastic being the only giveaway.

Any attempt to chop wild tobacco led to more tobacco springing up and a chest-tightening wheeze that foreboded heart damage. Those who'd worked clearing it related health scares, and I felt a fist clench in my chest every time I chopped. Just here and there clumps of kanuka and manuka promised long-term regeneration, a future hope based on the idea of gorse being shaded and withering in a screened forest, which was Rob Morton's way, a tactic in harmony with ecology and looking beyond the human lifespan. Another friend, Rob Fenwick, reclaiming hundreds of acres of island land, described the Hauraki Gulf as the weed capital of the world, with passionfruit, kiwi fruit, hakea, jasmine, you name it, going wild. No weedicides, no herbicides, though. Just letting one army of control, the indigenous, defeat another for the long term. Letting seed-eating wood pigeons drop what they ate and a pattern of interaction develop.

Each summer for six years we did more tree plantings, cut gorse, dug out tobacco weed. It was always rushed, temporary, token, although for everything put in or ripped out a blessing was made over the profusion and gifts of life. Rob Morton took wild cultivars of olive trees from other islands and we planted around sixty. Ironically they thrived where the gorse, a nitrogen enricher, grew thickest, and some of the best disappeared from view almost before the eyes, in the time lapse film that was the overrunning of Ake Ake. Leaving the job to a friendly neighbour the year Susie was ill, good work was obliterated by the time we came back, and a sense of nothing much done at all conveyed unfairly to someone who'd tried on our behalf.

Then there we were at Ake Ake again, wondering where last year's vision was gone. To keep the olives intact, there was Susie wielding a machete or breathlessly making a swipe with a brush-hook in brave attempts to stem the prickly tide. There was I, leaning over a spade and removing jellylike, waterlogged clay from a pug-hole where a tree floated rather than firmly corked in. Either we should beat a retreat, run goats, or call in an army, I declared. So the debate ran back and forth—but anyway, soon it was time to come back to Australia again.

When I wrote about New Zealand for a travel supplement I rhapsodised the differences on a kind of score card, All Blacks 100, Wallabies 0:

'The water is silken smooth, the stars are skeined by mist, there are no lights on the shore, which is unpeopled, no sounds apart from the purring outboard and the knock of yacht tackle on masts. No cries of mournful night birds, no all-pervading threat of summer smoke. The tide streams in, filling the inlets with its long fingers, slapping among the mangroves, carrying the splash of fish, flowing from the deep sea into the deep land, leaving traces of a way of living in the heart and habits of life.'

Disguised as flattery I deplored my missing connections:

What is it about you Kiwis, I wonder, you seem to have come a straight way through the psychic shoals, bypassing the gnarled dried roots of Australian bitterness and our blazing self-consuming cynicism. Rommel noticed in the North Africa campaign that the New Zealanders opposing him were clean tough fighters while Australians were treacherous and dirty . . .

You are a people who stepped here from the sea. Went up the gullies. Looked back at the sea. Land no sooner materialised before it broke away into archipelagoes and gulfs. You feel the mild summer air gathering through the passages and the sea-islands, breathing along with you the flow of the tide in the dark.'

And then, without quite realising it, I admitted to being hypnotised:

'At the ends of streets and along suburban bays people go swimming in a thoughtful, dreamy fashion. There's always water for Aucklanders to walk down to, they don't sprint into a surf and flail the waves and re-emerge puffing and blowing as if it's a contest with death. They stand in it up to their knees island-fashion, up to their waists, dressed in t-shirts and shorts or with skirts tucked up. A girl waits on the rocks with a plastic supermarket bag while a boy gathers shellfish. He troughs around like a dog in the gutters between rocks. A family group stands ankle-deep in earnest discussion and lovers softly fin along, two heads following the pull of the star-tides. While here comes a Tongan or a Cook Islander: he rolls up his trouser legs and steps into the water, reaches down and splashes handfuls of water onto his moon face as if in a ritual. After a long staring pause he returns to the beach and strips down to red underpants. Then he surges in, breast strokes, floats. A friend joins him and they have brief swimming races, they start to splash each other, skylark, and guffaw deliciously in their language. Later on the beach they stand gravely together and seem to be discussing a piece of local authority earthworks.'

One morning not long ago I struggled from a dream in which I looked up from under the earth and saw white, mushroom-like threads trailing down, taking hold. I was at Ake Ake in the frame bedroom of an unfinished house. We were there in July for tree planting and the island had a feeling of being closed down for winter. The previous week there'd been rain, and all the previous day we'd been out planting, and the day before that. The soil in the gully writhed with worms as the spades went in. Where the worst weed growth exploded we'd contracted heavy machinery with a flail and a mulcher. On the track to the beach, formerly dark and tangled, light came from a broken-open sky. Everywhere tobacco weed and gorse had been knocked down, chewed up, flung around until the place resembled a war zone. Repeated attacks reduced formerly impassable trunks and stalks to a prickly compost. Susie blocked her ears to the roar, closed her eyes, and said a prayer for damage done in passing. Formerly impassable on the western hill, the ground was now silvered, flung open. Cloud-shadows rippled along where the new plantings went in. Among thickets of wild tobacco we'd made a decision and agreed to selective use of herbicides—painting the stumps with a dichloram-diesel mixture and spraying moth plant seedlings with Roundup when they appeared like pea sprouts.

Trees from Rob Morton's nursery came on Tony King-Turner's truck. It was like a float in an agricultural show, waving with tightly-packed fronds. Tony was a track-builder and landscaper who planted with the help of a Czech traveller, Jiri. It felt like farming as I remembered it; I was up to my elbows in it. I spaded alongside them trying to keep pace, but Jiri lost me, he was a driven worker, so fast and hard he went almost on all fours from tree to tree, cigarette hanging from a pale lip and knees scrabbling the ground at speed. When he followed the chainsaw and crawled under bushes with the diesel bucket and paintbrush treating stumps it was too late to worry about anything. The Hauraki Gulf was the weed capital of the world and if scorching the earth could be described as being done judiciously then even that moment was past. Rain threatened and God help vulnerable species if the herbicide ran.

All day I found myself lingering back along the track, looking at the sets of trees awaiting planting. I still wasn't sure of names, maybe never would be, but I hardly believed what I saw. Which was?

This one's leaves like helicopter blades. That one's leaves gleaming like polished, open shells. Another's leaves like tough, plasticised tongues studded on a stick. The ferns had green, grublike central coils, and palm leaves were tough as hacked tin. Any way of describing them makes them seem strange but they weren't so strange any more. I seemed to have known them before, going back a long time—this was how the feeling came to me when it came.

# INTO THE LIGHT

'Was it possible to know nothing about trees and yet experience with certainty what they were? To know nothing in the same way we know just rudiments of people—yet readily love them, possessed by the certainty of knowing them?'

PUTTING THE tree's age at around seventy or eighty when I first saw it I was wrong—calculating age in trees egotistically through the human lifespan. But the tree was older, perhaps two hundred years, or three, or four, and I should have known—the fall of a leaf was a whisper to the living.

We wrote philosophies, built faiths, and took every kind of comfort from trees. They gave language to our existence as we put down roots, stretched our limbs, budded in infancy and were felled in old age. They were mute companions to our lives and worshipped beyond ourselves as the better part of balance and aspiration. They offered steadiness and long patience even as we failed in those. They were meeting points and sites of rough justice. They gave the idea and supplied the material for shelter. They offered an image of completion, which was an illusion, but it was enough. Theirs was a whisper in the wind to the human ear both tragic and hopeful. Civilisation grew from exploiting, destroying, venerating and looking back on them. Trees led us to ourselves and we stood against them trunk to trunk, arms upon branches, our thoughts tangled in the stars.

Because a tree bloomed seasonally we felt its body like our own. A tree stood still and yet suffered change. A tree growing old grew down into itself. Trees could not heal wounds, only cover them up. Trees were magnificent survivors. Trees got used. Trees behaved erratically under stress. Trees strove to fulfil an ideal shape but were twisted out of it by pressures of existence.

'There is a beautiful type of neglect of the perfectness of the Earth's beauty, by reason of the passions of men, in that picture of Paolo Uccello's of the battle of Sant Egidio, in which the armies meet on a country road beside a hedge of wild roses; the tender red flowers tossing above the helmets, and glowing between the lowered lances.'

Whole sections of tree died and the tree still lived; limbs fell off; the trunk shattered; roots flew into the air after a storm and the tree re-rooted itself. The oldest wood was in the core of the tree and the tree became younger towards the outside. The pith at the centre of a new twig was gradually enclosed in the centre of a trunk many metres across. The tree grew by placing a covering of wood over the whole of itself while the old tree remained held inside. Even in old age when the tree started dying at the top it continued coating itself with living material and sending out shoots. The part of the tree that lived was a thin material of bark and inner bark covering a skeleton of wood. Buds broke out lower down having awaited their moment in tissue.

Visiting my friend in the spinal unit he asked me how many trees would grow on five acres. Lying there paralysed from the neck down, smiling and talking about trees, it didn't matter to him for those few minutes that he was a 'ventilated quad' (what he remembered each morning when he woke—imagine it). The block was bare and maybe this was something he could do when at last they took him home, manage hundreds of trees into existence and oversee every aspect of their lives—olives, nuts, citrus. I pictured him on his five acres after his workmates built the house for him, getting around in an electric wheel-chair on shaded paths damp with sprinkler throw.

'From every leaf there was one slender fibre, or at least a fibre's thickness of wood, that descended through shoot, through spray, through branch, through stem and through trunk into root. It lost nothing of its energy until, mining through the darkness, it took hold in cleft of rock and depth of earth, as extended as the sweep of its green crest in the free air.'

A burnt-out eucalypt with a hollow inside balanced on a sandstone cliff-edge of the Blue Mountains. It was held upright by a flow of bark like a bucket of paint poured down. Embattled leaves made a stark headdress against the sky. Yet as long as photosynthesis kept working and water was available the tree kept growing, producing new wood to maintain the water-carrying link between roots and leaves. A physical pump action drew what scant water there was—enough—up through the inert, almost entirely dead material—wood— which was so thin it was only a shell.

The roots of trees were fingers taking the earth, clenching for support and scrounging for nourishment. The Caribbean 'knee' tree lifted a root in badly drained soil and avoided waterlogging by this method. Trees drew water into their roots in wet areas and released water through roots into dry areas. They pumped, breathed, and the air was changed.

Even in the dry forest, trees were columns of water. It was hard to credit this function of their lives. They stood on a bare-earth floor of ant mounds and grasstree spears. Their leaves hung down, sharp-angled to the sun. There was no movement anywhere, just the crackle of twigs and the desolate call of a crow. Meantime moisture trickled upwards and fed the leaves in the economy of life.

A friend went out in the morning when the frost was minus five. The sun burned white. She looked twice at the tree at the end of her yard and called the children out. 'There was no sun yet, the tree was in shade,' she told me in wonder, 'but I swear the tree gave out warmth. Its trunk was surrounded by shimmers of air movement, a mirage.' She made a shape in the air with her hands—the column of the tree.

As the tree grew, producing flowers and seeds, it required energy. When this energy was obtained from foods stored in the wood such as starch, oxygen was needed to release the energy from the starch in the process of respiration observed in all living things.

So the tree breathed.

I heard from a friend, who heard it from someone else, that a certain tree sucked up so much water that when someone else again put their ear to the trunk they heard the sound of water trickling up through the wood.

Was it possible to know nothing about trees and yet experience with certainty what they were? To know nothing in the same way we know just rudiments of people—yet readily love them, possessed by the certainty of knowing them?

Watching the battery input on the solar inverter react to light was to feel the leaf reacting to sunlight. An oscillating torrent of amps formed sugars within seconds as the thought went running through me, making the connection.

*

Trees were the prism of light varying itself in matter. Leaves turned to the food-generator of the sun:

'In very large trees, leaves were counted up to five million in number—making a mass of constantly adjusting surfaces. In deciduous trees, as leaves started to die in autumn, there was a tactical retreat, and re-usable proteins and chlorophyll were broken down and drawn back into the tree. Leaves changed colour because their greens were gone with the chlorophyll, allowing the leaf to turn yellow from pigments previously masked. Likewise with red pigments, which mixed with the yellows forming oranges, reds, purples, blues.'

Many beautiful effects derived from the tree's adaptations were defects to the sawmiller. Various names diminished the most embattled and characterful trees—'unsound pith', 'cone holes', 'needle trace', 'encased knots', 'gum veins', 'gum pockets'.

A section of sawn eucalypt thrown away resembled a painting of a sacked city following a fiery dawn, when glass towers were melted to amber and bloodlike beads marked an area of growth rings.

Coolabah trees went walking on a night of low moon on a floodplain of the Darling River. Out beyond the shearers' quarters they gathered like a population coming in, getting home through the river mist.

Still half asleep I went back to my bunk and folded myself in dreams. Between the trees and my dreaming about them there was no division.

I remembered a dream from years before, opposite in feeling:

'Heavy-footed, wrapped in slimy furs, the accusers plodded through trees and climbed the gravelly slope to my window. They loitered in dark reproachful groups tapping on glass. Above them, behind, the stars they arrived from gathered and drifted. Their leader turned, raised a sleeve to the glass in a gloomy gesture. Alive in his hand were the yellowy seeds of failure.'

The boy kept saying no, resisting what his parents asked of him. Creating difficulties for himself he was all hard shell, all seed casing. Any view of him not asserted by himself felt like an imposed shape before any shape was begun. Yet who he was he couldn't say, didn't even feel, mostly. He went on building protection around himself until the character of the shell seemed everything about him that mattered. And he thought that was all that was going to happen in his life.

I was drawn to trees without knowing why. 'Longing to grow, I looked outside myself, and the tree inside me grew.' I read these words and wanted understanding. If there was a physical tree in an actual place, in myself, where was it?

\*

Asking the question seeded an answer. Branch, root, hand, step, sensation—it was an urge complete in itself, an outburst unfolding. No need then for any parable of trees. The direct speech of feeling was allegorical, and irreplaceable by anything else.

Planting out was taking trees from a nursery tray and putting them in the earth. Planting out was kneeling, breaking open ground, getting dirty, smeared with soil, holding a trembling seedling in a work routine that was agricultural and primitive, sacramental and sexual. Planting out was the physical character of the spiritual tree continued.

Light, upon which trees depended, and which the tree's function could be botanically described as existing to catch, stood blazing above the tree and transformed it.

The living principle of the tree was in the painting, 'Nude descending a staircase', in which dimensions of life were energised by the human trunk moving through time. 'The balance of the bough of a tree was quite as subtle as that of a figure in motion.'

The old man lay in his hospital bed hot-handedly thinking of nothing but seeding. And there was the tree, feeding itself to the edge of his awareness.

'To find nature herself, all her likenesses have to be shattered; and the further in, the nearer the actual thing.'

The bloodwood at Quondong stock camp lived in my thoughts, *Eucalyptus dampierii* molten in the first light, bowed by heat soon after. Under the rough outer bark prising itself off like scabs were small, almost tiled powdery pale brown and grey surfaces marked by old branch wounds closed over. Higher up the tiling was more marked and showed in a thicker outer bark, scabby but chocolate-squared with an appearance of being glued by hand.

When someone said, 'Why should I plant a tree if I'll never see it grown?' I thought, look at the seedlings in the moist ground, they are beseeching.

Trees roused turmoil in the night. Wind roared through their branches. In a night of storm, anxieties were sounded in the trumpet blast of leaves. In the morning stillness their voice was gone and the tree was a blue vase of light.

Trees were an element of infinity lending shape and style to ordinary being. 'Depression is a husk covering the seed of all that is holy. The value of delight is its ability to combat the destructive power of the imagination.'

\*

Trees and people were of the same spark, the essence of light made conspicuous in material existence. A tree's woody skeleton and the human frame returned the gift, craving light for growth.

Nothing until the end stopped the tree taking light and sending the light down through itself.

Watching a baby in its first year of life, the comparison with a seedling crinkling open or a bud unfolding was made.

'It is clearly possible to do without them, for the great companionship of the sea and sky are all that sailors need; and many a noble heart has been taught the best it had to learn between dark stone walls. Still if human life be cast among trees at all, the love borne to them is a sure test of its purity.'

Buds appeared along the living branch, and which of these buds flourished and by how much determined the shape of the tree. Holding a twig against the tree was to see the tree.

In their school magazine the Year 12 girls stated their life's wishes: 'To touch a star'; 'To be infectiously happy'; 'To be taller than the tallest poppy'; 'To be satisfied with my life when I reflect in old age'.

*

As for ourselves, so for the tree. 'Everything in the world must excel itself to be itself.'

'The young girl lies straight, bending neither at waist nor knee, the sheet rising and falling over her in a narrow unbroken wave, like the shape of the coverlid of the last sleep, when the turf scarcely rises.'

This also was the tree.

The tree goes flying along without straying from its place; the tree goes talking in the wind, tossing its crown; the tree awaits inspiration. The tree creates a balancing act, a strain of opposing forces. Under pressure a tree falls in on itself. Then it is renewed for a time. Then it dies.

'Some big old Boabs become quite hollow, but still they bear foliage and continue to flower and fruit. I have seen one, about eighty kilometres west of Fitzroy Crossing, that has spread so wide and lost so much of its filling that it seems to have forgotten that it is a tree. The trunk now consists of a rambling, lumpy wall enclosing space. The interior is open to the skies, and you can peer into it through holes high in the wall. In the bottom of the sunny hollow grow grasses and other plants whose seeds have found their way inside and germinated. Were there only a doorway, you could stable horses in this tree, and not have to worry immediately about supplying them with feed. And still the tree lives.'

At night I climbed the ringbarked paddocks with a galvanised iron bucket of hot ashes, carrying fire from tree to tree, shovelling coals through the doorways in roots. Fired trees smoked all day like old people's cottages. Next night they blazed red, collapsing in pillars of flame. Before daylight they poured themselves down in piles of embers that glowed like cities.

'On the lower slopes, and far up every glen, the Spanish chestnut-trees stood each foursquare to heaven under its tented foliage. Some were planted, each on its own terrace no larger than a bed; some, trusting in their roots, found strength to grow and prosper and be straight and large upon the rapid slopes of the valley; others, where there was a margin to the river, stood marshalled in a line and mighty like the cedars of Lebanon. Yet even where they grew most thickly they were not to be thought of as a wood, but as a herd of stalwart individuals; and the dome of each tree stood forth separate and large, and as it were a little hill, from among the domes of its companions.'

In midlife Boris Pasternak dismissed his earlier style as obscure and pretentious. But everything could be said of his work that could be said of a tree, that in it the natural seemed supernatural. So his earlier work survived the self-condemnation. All that was past remained present, with life returning 'with as little reason as once it was so strangely interrupted'.

He wrote of Mayakovsky:

'It was as if he existed on the day following a terrific spiritual life lived through for use in all subsequent events, and everyone came upon him in the sheaf of its unbending sequences.'

Digging out the old well, the deeper I went the smaller the ring of sky grew above me. In that circle the growth-tips of poplars were visible. Meantime below, their roots were massed like heathen hair, red and furious, ball-hard as I axed them free. Sandy-blue water trickled into my boots. My head sank from sight, and anyone passing, calling, missed me. What if I drowned, smothered, got buried alive as the walls caved in? My mother told me how well-diggers moved around the countryside in the nineteenth century. I made a decision, trusted my predecessors, and pressed on with it. At intervals I used the firefighting pump to suck the well dry. The stonework of granite blocks was smooth and glistened freshly after one hundred and forty years. Digging out the old well was a satisfaction I was unable put into words. It was all there in my hands, at night in my dreamless sleep.

Whenever I looked up, it was to remember who had planted those poplars years before. They'd started as thin whips when I first planted them. Now they were like wharf piles. Whenever I looked down, there I was tracking their roots. In the honeycomb rock at the bottom the roots kept unravelling. Scrawling against the sky, they were something I'd written.

\*

'Sometimes I cannot but think of the trees of the earth as capable of a kind of sorrow, in that imperfect life of theirs, as they opened their innocent leaves in the warm spring-time, in vain for men; and all along the dells of England her beeches cast their dappled shade only where the outlaw drew his bow, and the king rode his careless chase; and by the sweet French rivers their long ranks of poplar waved in the twilight, only to show the flames of burning cities on the horizon, through the tracery of their stems; amidst the fair defiles of the Appenines, the twisted olive-trunks hid the ambushes of treachery; and on their valley meadows, day by day, the lilies which were white at dawn were washed with crimson at sunset.'

Trees clung to life and kept thrusting out growth to the end. The moment of completion was the beginning of the end of the tree's life, as it died from the top downwards while still obeying the imperative to stay fully alive. When a tree canopy reached maximum size it was balanced with its resources but the tree continued adding new layers of wood. It was a process of dying down, redefining dying as growth, that may have taken centuries after the tree reached its prime— ensuring that trees stood ever beyond us even as they sheltered and warmed us.

The aliveness of trees was a discipline and an economy, whereas our human aliveness led us to deny (in trying to overcome) environmental effects. This way we made ourselves richer to the detriment of our surrounds. We burned trees in our hearths and burned them for agriculture. We gained room for contemplation (otherwise no culture). But our comfort in denial was transitory. The tree submitted to a more ruthless penalty and perfected its beauty, branches bared to the light of the sun.

Light, upon which the tree depended, and which the tree's function was botanically described as being solely to catch, stood blazing behind the tree and the tree disappeared.

# NOTES, SOURCES &
# ACKNOWLEDGMENTS

The lines beginning 'No genuine book has a first page' (on p. vii) are from Boris Pasternak, quoted in *Twentieth Century Russian Poetry*, edited by Albert C. Todd and selected by Yevgeny Yevtushenko (Doubleday, New York, 1993).

In 'Planting Out' and throughout this book many botanical observations are gratefully acknowledged to Peter Thomas, *Trees: Their Natural History* (Cambridge, 2000); Andreas Feininger, *Trees* (The Viking Press, New York, 1968); John Salmon, *The Native Trees of New Zealand* (A.H. and A.W. Reed, Wellington, 1980); and John Ruskin, *Modern Painters* 1843–1860, Volume V (George Allen, London, 1897) (all further references to Ruskin are from the same source).

'The tree grew not by stetching . . .' is from Ruskin.

The image of moths is from the photograph 'Moths on a windowpane', by Olive Cotton (1995).

The lines starting 'Too much rain' are the poem 'Crown', by Kay Ryan, published in *The New Yorker*, 22 May 2000.

'Where the Fire Has Been' was originally commissioned for Gregg Borschmann's *The People's Forest* (The People's Forest Press, Blackheath, New South Wales, 1999). The family history in this chapter owes much to my mother, Dr Lorna McDonald (b. 1916), writer, historian, and exemplary country-woman; and to my uncle, Rev Graeme Bucknall (1909–1997). In relation to my father, Rev Hugh Fraser McDonald (1909–81), when I ask 'What was his tree?' it is a question of a kind men put to their fathers usually too late for any personal exchange. (Though when E.O. Wilson, in his autobiography *Naturalist*, wondered of his long dead father what his ideal was—the template he fell short of fulfilling, which the son could use as an example years later—it was a kind of reply.)


'Life of a Tree Planter' is dedicated to the memory of Wilf Crane and I thank Colleen Crane very much for accepting it.


Writing thumbnail sketches of inspired tree planters was my original plan for this book. For 'Bush Gardener' and 'The Red Bull' I thank Tom Wyatt and Robert Campbell. My thanks go to Tom Carment for 'Trees Without Names'.


I am grateful to Phil Cheney for 'Signs for the Gate'; refer-ences are from *Grassfires: Fuel, Weather, and Fire Behaviour* (CSIRO Publishing, Collingwood, 1997) by Phil Cheney and Andrew Sullivan; 'Living With Fire' in *Think Trees, Grow Trees* (AGPS, Canberra, 1985); and *Burning Bush: A Fire History of Australia* (Henry Holt and Company, New York,

1991) by Stephen J. Pyne. The quotes starting 'Once torched, the burning bush . . .' and 'The fluffy ash accepts the falling seed . . .' are both from Pyne.

'The Story of Rosie' is a true account with names changed, while 'Secrets of Tu Bi-Shevat' and 'The Park' are fiction.

'Wild Man in Landscape' is based on the poetry of Roland Robinson (1912–92). Many of the words and phrases used are derived from three books of his poetry, *Language of the Sand* (1949), *Tumult of the Swans* (1953), collected in *Deep Well* (Edwards and Shaw, Sydney, 1962). I am also indebted to *The Drift of Things* (Macmillan, Melbourne, 1972), the first volume of his autobiography.

'The Seed' is based on the early poems of Judith Wright (1915–2000). Many of the words and phrases are derived from *The Moving Image* (Angus & Robertson, Sydney, 1946) and *Woman to Man* (Angus & Robertson, Sydney, 1949).

In 'At Sheep Camp' the image of galahs like town councillors is from a poem 'Galahs' in *The Talking Clothes* (Angus & Robertson, Sydney, 1966) by William Hart–Smith (1911–90).

In 'At Ake Ake', the W.H. Auden poem, 'If I Could Tell You,' is from *Collected Poems* (Faber & Faber, London, 1994).

The following notes refer to 'Into the Light'.

In this final chapter the botanical references are the same as for 'Planting Out', namely: Thomas, Feininger, Salmon and Ruskin (see note on page 173).

'The falling leaf is a whisper to the living' is an English proverb.

'There is a beautiful type of neglect . . .' is from Ruskin, as is 'From every leaf there was one slender fibre . . .'.

Some mangroves have 'knee' roots (pneumatophores), as does the south-east USA bald or swamp cypress. There is a Caribbean 'knee' tree in the Sydney Botanic Gardens, but the ground is not flooded and so the knees aren't up.

Angela Marshall saw the shimmering tree at Majors Creek in the unusually cold winter of 2000.

'In very large trees, leaves were counted up to five million in number . . .' is adapted, with changed tense, from Thomas.

The walking coolabah trees I wrote about in *Shearers' Motel* (1992, republished by Vintage, Sydney, 2001).

The dream described was the subject of a poem 'The Accusers' in my book *Airship* (University of Queensland Press, St Lucia, 1975), using almost identical wording as here.

The quotation 'Longing to grow . . .' is from a poem by Rainer Maria Rilke.

'The direct speech of feeling . . .' is an aphorism from Boris Pasternak.

'The balance of the bough . . .' is from Ruskin.

'To find nature herself . . .' is from Meister Eckhart, quoted in *The Tree of Life* by Roger Cook (Thames and

Hudson, London, 1974).

'Depression is a husk covering the seed . . .' is from Rabbi Nachman of Bratslav (1772–1811), quoted in *Rabbi Nachman's Stories*, translated by Aryen Kaplan (Breslov Research Institute, Jerusalem, 1983).

'It is clearly possible to do without them . . .' is a passage from Ruskin.

'Everything in the world must excel itself to be itself' is from Boris Pasternak, *I Remember, Sketch for an Autobiography*, translated by David Magarshack (Pantheon, New York, 1959).

'The young girl lies straight . . .' is Ruskin's description of Carpaccio's 'The Dream of Saint Ursula'.

The description of old Boab trees is by Pat Lowe, *Boab* (Lothian Books, Melbourne, 1998).

The description of chestnuts in the valley of the Tarn is from *Travels With a Donkey in the Cevennes*, 1879, by R.L. Stevenson.

Life returning 'with as little reason . . .' is from 'Zhivago's Poems' in *Doctor Zhivago*, by Boris Pasternak, translated by Max Hayward and Manya Harari (William Collins, London, 1958). The description of Mayakovsky is from *Safe Conduct*, by the same author (Moscow, 1931), translated by J.M. Cohen (London, 1945). 'When I was invited to say something about myself,' wrote Pasternak, 'I would start talking about Mayakovsky.'

'Sometimes I cannot but think of the trees of the earth as capable of sorrow . . .' is from Ruskin.